PIPE FITTINGS

NIPPLES

PIPE LENGTHS UP TO 22 FT.

STRAIGHT COUPLING

REDUCING COUPLING

COUPLING

NUT

CAP

STRAIGHT TEE

REDUCING TEE

STREET TEE

STRAIGHT CROSS

REDUCING CROSS

90° ELBOW

90° ELBOW

90° ELBOW

45° ELBOW

REDUCING ELBOW

90° STREET ELBOW

45° STREET ELBOW

45° Y-BEND

REDUCING TEE

REDUCER

UNION (3 PARTS)

PLUG

BUSHING

CAP

RETURN BEND

90°

45°

UNION ELBOWS

STREET

UNION TEES

PLUG

45° ELBOW

TEE

MEASURES OF CAPACITY

1 cup	=	8 fl oz
2 cups	=	1 pint
2 pints	=	1 quart
4 quarts	=	1 gallon
2 gallons	=	1 peck
4 pecks	=	1 bushel

STANDARD STEEL PIPE ((All Dimensions in inches)

Nominal Size	Outside Diameter	Inside Diameter	Nominal Size	Outside Diameter	Inside Diameter
1/8	0.405	0.269	1	1.315	1.049
1/4	0.540	0.364	1 1/4	1.660	1.380
3/8	0.675	0.493	1 1/2	1.900	1.610
1/2	0.840	0.622	2	2.375	2.067
3/4	1.050	0.824	2 1/2	2.875	2.469

WOOD SCREWS

LENGTH	GAUGE NUMBERS														
1/4 INCH	0	1	2	3											
3/8 INCH			2	3	4	5	6	7							
1/2 INCH			2	3	4	5	6	7	8						
5/8 INCH				3	4	5	6	7	8	9	10				
3/4 INCH					4	5	6	7	8	9	10	11			
7/8 INCH							6	7	8	9	10	11	12		
1 INCH							6	7	8	9	10	11	12	14	
1 1/4 INCH								7	8	9	10	11	12	14	16
1 1/2 INCH							6	7	8	9	10	11	12	14	16	18
1 3/4 INCH									8	9	10	11	12	14	16	18	20
2 INCH									8	9	10	11	12	14	16	18	20
2 1/4 INCH										9	10	11	12	14	16	18	20
2 1/2 INCH													12	14	16	18	20
2 3/4 INCH														14	16	18	20
3 INCH															16	18	20
3 1/2 INCH																18	20	24
4 INCH																18	20	24

WHEN YOU BUY SCREWS, SPECIFY (1) LENGTH, (2) GAUGE NUMBER, (3) TYPE OF HEAD—FLAT, ROUND, OR OVAL, (4) MATERIAL—STEEL, BRASS, BRONZE, ETC., (5) FINISH—BRIGHT, STEEL BLUED, CADMIUM, NICKEL, OR CHROMIUM PLATED.

Popular Mechanics

do-it-yourself encyclopedia

The complete, illustrated home reference guide from the world's most authoritative source for today's how-to-do-it information.

Volume 15

KNIVES

to

MARKSMANSHIP

HEARST DIRECT BOOKS

NEW YORK

Acknowledgements

The Popular Mechanics Encyclopedia is published with the consent and cooperation of POPULAR MECHANICS Magazine.

For POPULAR MECHANICS Magazine:

Editor-in-Chief: *Joe Oldham*
Managing Editor: *Bill Hartford*
Special Features Editor: *Sheldon M. Gallager*
Automotive Editor: *Wade A. Hoyt, SAE*
Home and Shop Editor: *Steve Willson*
Electronics Editor: *Stephen A. Booth*
Boating, Outdoors and Travel Editor: *Timothy H. Cole*
Science Editor: *Dennis Eskow*

Popular Mechanics Encyclopedia

Project Director: *Boyd Griffin*
Manufacturing: *Ron Schoenfeld*
Assistant Editors: *Cynthia W. Lockhart
Peter McCann, Rosanna Petruccio*
Production Coordinator: *Peter McCann*

The staff of Popular Mechanics Encyclopedia is grateful to the following individuals and organizations:

Editor: *C. Edward Cavert*
Editor Emeritus: *Clifford B. Hicks*
Production: *Layla Productions*
Production Director: *Lori Stein*
Book Design: *The Bentwood Studio*
Art Director: *Jos. Trautwein*
Design Consultant: *Suzanne Bennett & Associates*
Illustrations: *AP Graphics, Evelyne Johnson Associates, Popular Mechanics Magazine, Vantage Art.*

Contributing Writers: Monte Burch, *Customize your hanging knife handle*, page 1796; Walter E. Burton, *Spoonholder lamp*, page 1834; *Turn plastic on your lathe*, page 1871; *Turning rings on a lathe*, page 1876; Tom Faulkner, *Zeroing-in a rifle*, page 1911; Ed Franzese, *Fluorescent lamp basics*, page 1816; Thomas A. Gauldin, *Garage door electric lock*, page 1897; Jackson Hand, *Long look at long ladders*, page 1809; Clifford B. Hicks, *Lawn care for the best lawn in your neighborhood*, page 1880; Len Hilts, *Landscaping that's down to earth*, page 1843; John H. Ingersoll, *Low-energy lighting saves money*, page 1820; J.A. Lackner, *Spanish style lamp*, page 1823; Sid Latham, *Customize your knife sheath*, page 1799; Wayne C. Leckey, *Candlestand lamp*, page 1825; Marshall Lincoln, *Target box that serves a double duty*, page 1914; George Nonte, *Ultimate test for your rifle*, page 1915; Don Shiner, *Magazine bucket*, page 1909; Elmer Verburg, *Cobbler's bench table lamp*, page 1829; Wilson G. Walters, *Collapsible leaf cart*, page 1891; Harry Wicks, *Game area lighting*, page 1836; *Night lighting transforms your yard*, page 1839; *Wood lathe tips from an expert*, page 1849; Jim Woods, *Pick the perfect knife*, page 1802.

Picture Credits: Popular Mechanics Encyclopedia is grateful to the following for permission to reprint their photographs: Halo Lighting-Cooper Industries, Inc., page 1814; General Electric/Tim Snider, page 1815.

ISBN 0-87851-168-7

Library of Congress 85-81760

10 9 8 7 6 5 4
PRINTED IN THE UNITED STATES OF AMERICA

Although every effort has been made to ensure the accuracy and completeness of the information in this book, Hearst Direct Books makes no guarantees, stated or implied, nor will they be liable in the event of misinterpretation or human error made by the reader, or for any typographical errors that may appear. WORK SAFELY WITH HAND TOOLS. WEAR SAFETY GOGGLES. READ MANUFACTURER'S INSTRUCTIONS AND WARNINGS FOR ALL PRODUCTS.

Contents

Customize your hunting-knife handle

■ A GOOD HUNTING KNIFE should fit your individual use and needs. And making one is not as difficult as you may think. For starters, good blades today are available from a variety of mail-order sources.

Almost anything can be used as the handle, including antler, bone, ivory or leather rings. However, one of the best materials and probably the easiest to work with is a heavy mineral wood such as amaranth, vermilion, zebrawood or ebony. These woods will not rot and are heavy enough to balance with the blade. The wood depicted in this article is amaranth—an extremely hard, oily wood that takes checkering or carving and finishes like a piece of fine metal. It is available in the inch thickness required for a good knife handle.

Best bet is to order a knife-blade catalog and select a blade. While you're waiting for it to arrive, trace its design and make sketches of a handle pattern to fit it.

The pattern shown could be adapted to most any knife, but the "three-finger" handle best suits a knife with a forefinger hole in the blade. Grasping the handle at the rear makes the knife front-heavy, ideal for lopping off tree limbs or hacking through bone when preparing meat. By moving your fingers up one notch, you have good control for delicate skinning operations.

Grind about 1¼ inches off the end of the tang. Make a template for the handle pattern out of cardboard, cut a block from the handle wood and glue the template in position. Make sure the block is absolutely square on all sides. Using a clamp to hold it upright and square, place the block in your drill press and bore for the tang. Be sure to measure the exact length of the tang and bore just a bit deeper. Make sure the hole doesn't "lean" to one side. You may have to grind the

tang a bit to make it fit properly. When the handle block fits on the tang with just a little persuasion, remove it and cut out the handle.

Next make the brass guard. The one shown was purposely kept small so you could get your forefinger into the notch on the blade. It is needed to butt the handle, providing a smooth transition from handle to blade. The guard should be about ⅛-inch thick and large enough to extend around the handle at least ³/₁₆ inch. Using a hacksaw, cut a brass square the size you wish

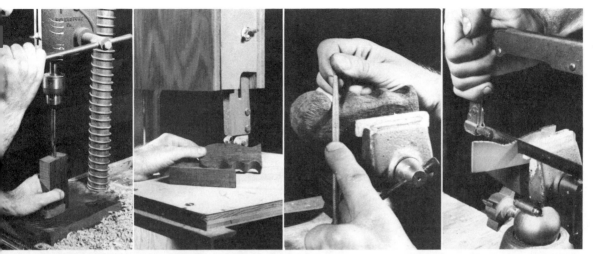

PATTERN FOR HANDLE is traced or glued on squared-hardwood block. Then (from left) block is held in clamp and tang hole bored. Handle shape is cut on a bandsaw or coping saw. Next, the handle is roughed to shape with rasps and files. Spacer guard is cut from brass stock to separate the handle from the forged metal guard.

your guard to be and bore it to fit over the tang. You may have to bore it oversize, as the tang widens at the base of the knife blade.

When you have it bored to fit over the tang and tight against the end of the blade, grind it in an oval determined by the shape of your knife handle. This is a grind-and-fit operation. Grind a bit off, place it on the tang and fit the handle until the oval is centered with blade and tang. Slide the brass guard in place. Mix a batch of epoxy

glue and force it into the tang hole in the handle. Then place the handle down on the tang and examine it from every angle to insure you have the brass guard positioned right and the handle square with the blade. Tap the end of the handle to seat it and let it set overnight.

Using finer grits of wet-or-dry sandpaper, finish the handle and guard. If you have a buffing wheel, polish the handle and guard to a satin sheen. Apply a good quality gunstock finish—oil

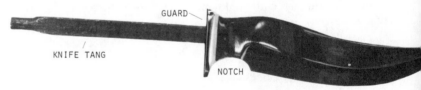

GUARD

KNIFE TANG

NOTCH

FOREFINGER NOTCH on the forged guard blade makes for excellent skinning control. The knife tang fits into the handle as outlined in the pattern on ½-inch squares below.

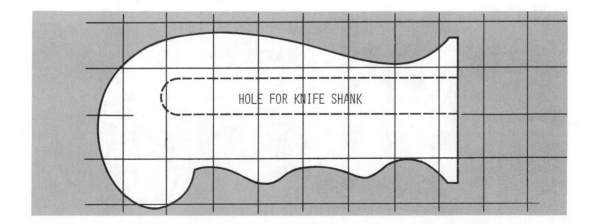

HOLE FOR KNIFE SHANK

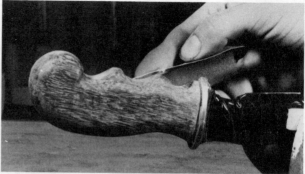

FORCE EPOXY GLUE into the bored hole. Place the brass guard over blade tang and press tang into the hole. Let it sit overnight. Next day, put taped blade in vise, sand handle and brass guard with progressively finer paper.

or spray epoxy—and lightly polish with paste wax and a soft cloth.

You may wish to checker your handle so that it will be much easier to hold when wet or in cold weather. Do not use any checkering finer than 18 lines to the inch. It's beautiful, but won't help much on your grip. Amaranth and other mineral woods are especially hard, so hone your checkering tools sharp before you start.

Using a scriber or nail, lay out the checkering design, scratching it lightly into the finish. Using the diamond template, lay out the first line and cut it fairly deep with the single cutter. Switch to the double cutter and score the lines in one direc-tion. When all lines are cut in one direction, find the first line for the other direction with the template and cut it. Proceed as before and when all lines are scored, use the single-line cutter to deepen them and make the diamonds sharp and even.

When the checkering is completed, cut the outline using a fine veiner chisel. Checker the other side of the handle to match the first and with fine sandpaper, knock the sharp burrs off the edges of the diamonds. Apply finish to the checkered handle and polish and burnish it to a fine sheen.

APPLY QUALITY gunstock finish, spray epoxy or oil type. Then checker the knife handle for better grip, spray checkering with the finish and remove black electrician's tape used to protect the blade while you were working on handle.

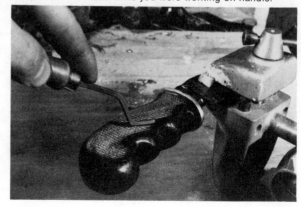

Customize your knife sheath

■ A FINE KNIFE DESERVES the best sheath possible to protect it. Here is how to make a beautiful custom sheath in leather. Many knife artisans have no interest in leather work. They would rather leave this task to someone else. This part of the job is a creative challenge.

Choose a good piece of ⅞-oz. vegetable-tanned leather. This type of leather can be easily formed to the contours of your knife, is excellent for tooling, and provides a better fit than chrome-tanned or other leathers. Because it can absorb water well, it is good to work with, but must be handled with great care. If you happen to touch it with tools or even your fingernails while it is wet, you will leave marks that are almost impossible to remove.

The pattern

Proper fit is the result of making a careful pattern. Take your time and be as exact as possible.

Start by laying the knife on a piece of paper. Draw its outline, plus the outline of the sheath. Next, use dividers to mark a stitch line around the edge of the pattern. Stitch holes are then marked along the stitch line, about ⅛ in. apart. An ordinary kitchen fork is a good tool to use for this job.

With the pattern as a guide, the sheath is cut out. A sharp knife works fine, but you might also try a modeler's knife blade, heavy shears or special leather-worker's head knife. Stitch holes are indented into the leather with an awl, but it is not necessary for these holes to go all of the way through at this point.

Use a hobbyist's motor tool or drill press to make the holes for the stitches. An awl can be used, but don't try to force it or a needle through the three layers of leather around the edge. Instead, a small bit slightly larger than the needle should be used. This will make a neat row of stitch holes, and final stitching will be considerably easier.

Edges are now rounded, beveled and trimmed. Fine sandpaper (400 to 600 grit) can be used. Rub gently to actually burnish the edges down and smooth them off.

Now is the time to do any decorative tooling, stamping or carving. Artwork and embossing at this stage can add real beauty and value to your knife sheath if done correctly and carefully. For these steps, the leather is dampened, then left until it feels almost dry. Be careful not to spill any paint or scratch the leather because you won't be able to remove these marks.

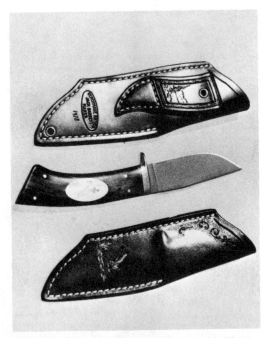

SHEATH HAS hand-tooled decorations, molded front for snug fit, grommet at bottom of back for rain drain, and hole in loop for hanging in display case.

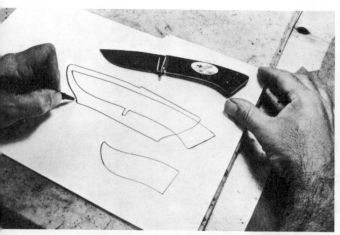

PATTERN for sheath is developed by making outline sketch around knife. Outer edge of sheath is drawn around it. Belt loop must be drawn first, too.

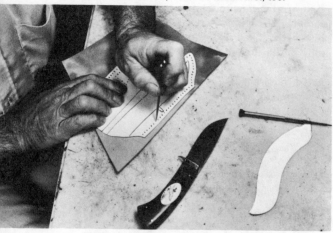

STITCH LINE is first scribed inside outer edge of sheath pattern with dividers. Stitch-hole placements may be marked with fork.

SPACER WELT is then cut and fitted into sheath. It will hold knife in place, keep blade away from threads. Use a small drill for stitch holes.

Stitching

Many experts favor the saddle stitch, using nylon thread and a needle on each side.

First, the top of the belt loop is sewn to the back of the sheath. Then a hole is carefully punched and lined with a brass grommet. This hole allows for hanging for display in a gun-and-knife cabinet.

Another grommet hole also goes in the back bottom of the sheath. This second hole is a drain hole in case a hunter or fisherman is wearing it in a downpour or falls in a stream.

The belt loop is grooved slightly at the fold. It is best to shave it down a bit with a skiving knife and stitch it down at the bottom to make a firm, tight loop.

An important part of the sheath is known as a *welt*. Its function is to keep the top and bottom of the sheath apart and prevent the blade from cutting through the threads. Once the welt is cut, the parts are assembled without any stitching to test the fit.

With holes drilled for stitches and all of the parts stained, they are now laced together. Use tight saddle stitches, as well as a few back stitches to secure the pieces in place. Then hold a flame to the trimmed end of each nylon thread. This will help prevent it from fraying and further lock it in.

Forming and baking

Next come more customizing steps that can give your sheath a professional appearance. Start by trimming all the rough edges with a very sharp knife. Next, slightly dampen these edges and rub them with fine sandpaper. Final polishing is done with a piece of bone, ivory, Micarta or hardwood.

Wet-forming is done to get a tight fit. To do this, dampen the leather enough so that you can form the sheath to the contour of the knife with your fingers. Be especially careful to make no fingernail scratches, as they may leave permanent marks. After completing this task, allow the sheath to dry overnight.

A final wax process may also be desired. This will give the leather a handsome appearance and make it waterproof. To about 4 liquid ounces of molten paraffin, add ¾ oz. of saddle oil (a blend of lanolin and silicon). *Heat this mixture carefully, preferably over an electric hot plate, since it catches fire easily.*

Once it is hot and well mixed, carefully brush it on the inside and outside of the entire sheath. Never dip the sheath in the solution; it will absorb too much. (And never coat the mixture on

DECORATIVE sketches and tooling are added. Paint, even fingernail scratches, cannot be removed from leather.

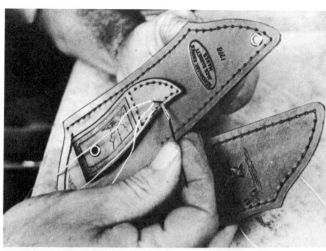

SADDLE stitching, with needles pushed in from opposite sides, secures belt loop to sheath. Top and bottom, with welt, are then stitched together.

leather boots; it will seal the pores, and you might get frostbite.)

Finishing the job

After the sheath has been brush-coated, place a stick or rod in it and rotate it over a low flame on the stove. This will help melt and draw the wax right into the fibers of the leather. Then set the oven at about 170°. Place the sheath on a piece of aluminum foil and leave it in the oven for 15 minutes. When you take it out, examine it thoroughly. If you see any remaining blobs of wax on the surface or in the stitching, remove and smooth them with a toothpick.

If you have followed the procedure outlined here, you should have developed a fine sheath. Your finished product may not include the embossing and artwork shown here, but there is no doubt you'll take pride in your own customized sheath, a perfect fit for your favorite knife.

Pick a perfect knife

■ UNTIL RECENTLY, only a few personal-knife types were popular. There was the pocket-knife that could be used for whittling and the multiblade camper's knife of the Boy Scout type. The hunter's sheath knife was related to the Army and Marine fighting and survival knives of several years ago. These, in turn, were modified varieties of Bowie knives, with century-old heavy

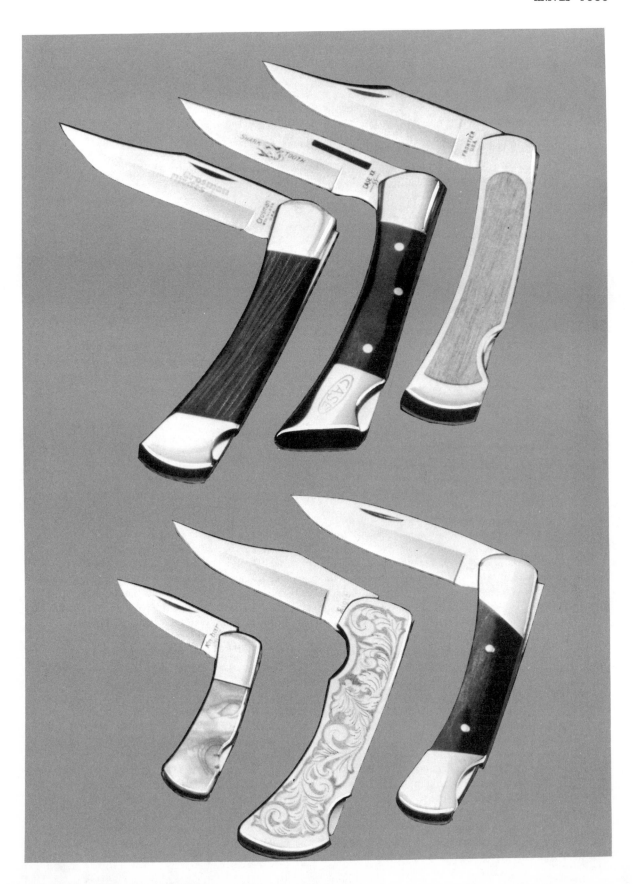

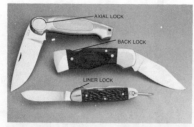

LOCKING folders are popular.

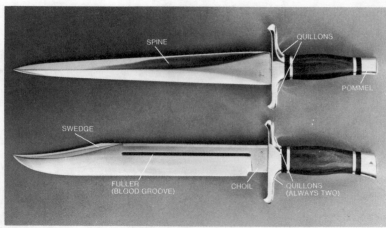

DOUBLE-EDGE Arkansas Bowie (top) and Classic Bowie knife (bottom).

CUSTOM KIT and rigid knives kit are ready for home finishing.

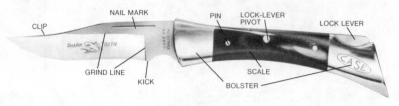

SHARK TOOTH model attracts collectors.

blade and clip-point designs. Today's knives are different, and the finest are much more expensive.

A material that has influenced considerable change is stainless steel. No longer is it a metal with unpredictable qualities that appeared shortly after World War II. Now, an increasing number of quality knives made worldwide are stainless. Generally, U.S. factory-made blades use 440 stainless, while the several hundred custom knifemakers employ 440C or 154CM.

Plastics for handles

The plastics of modern technology have also had considerable influence on knife construction. Natural handle materials—horn, bone and ivory—are still in demand for some expensive knives, but for various reasons are in short supply. To meet a growing demand, plastics such as Lexan, Delrin and Micarta are the answer. None of these are new. Lexan is the practically bulletproof material that is sometimes used for cashiers' cages. Delrin has been cast and machined

into high-strength aircraft components for years. Micarta, a phenolic resin developed by Westinghouse, has been in use for electric insulators since the 1930s. All of these machine relatively easily, take a smooth finish, are warm to the touch, and will outlast the steel in the blades. Almost any knife you buy today will have a plastic handle—and it probably will be a good one.

Better locks

Perhaps the biggest design improvement has been the blade lock for the folders. It has put new safety into folding knives, and has helped personal knives become socially acceptable. This wasn't the case at the start. The first lock-back folders, generally considered to be the product of Buck Knives in California, were large knives with husky blades. For several years, "buck knife" was the generic description of a lock-back folder from any manufacturer. The big folders rode in equally big snap-flap pouches, frequently hanging from the belts of some members of our rougher social element. In time, the knives be-

BROWNING South Pass is in presentation box. Cam III assortment (below) has three-bladed belt buckle.

STAGHANDLE No. 3 Hunter is famous Randall.

GERBER'S folder has Bolt-Action lock.

WESTMARK 702 is a fine knife.

SWISS ARMY knife has lock.

NEW FOLDER is in Camillus Wildlife Series.

came smaller and more finely finished, disappeared into pockets rather than belt pouches, and then emerged in belt pouches once again as they became respectable. Now, a lock-back folding knife in a belt pouch is as common as a wristwatch in the everyday dress of many men, and a few women, in all manner of occupations.

Folding blade lock

There are a number of variations in lock locations and advertising names, but the folding-blade lock is usually a lever that runs the length of the handle back. When this lever is depressed, the forward end that engages a notch in the blade tang pivots up and releases the blade.

A simple and less expensive device is the liner lock, a springy brass divider between blades or handle scale and blade, that snaps into place behind the blade tang when the blade is fully extended. To close the blade, the liner is warped aside with the thumb. More complicated and expensive is the axial lock. This is primarily offered by custom knifemakers, but Gerber Blades and Kershaw Cutlery, both in Oregon, have axial lock models. Blade locks are not new, and some antique folders have clever ones.

Better shapes

While the latest popular blade designs aren't brand new, one that was rediscovered about 25 years ago and dubbed the "drop point" is a current favorite and a good compromise shape.

Knife blade shapes are identified by point style and location. Hold the knife horizontal with the edge down. If the blade back is straight to the point, the style is "straight point." It's a good skinning and slicing blade, and knives so equipped are classed as skinners, although there are specialized shapes that do a better job.

Point types

If the back of the blade curves up, the point is called a "sweeping" or "swept" point. If it angles down to a point below the blade back or is in a curve that resembles a ski jump, the blade has a "clip" or "clipped" point. If the downward curve is like that of a bullet trajectory and the point is more than midway down the blade, it is the "dropped" point. When the blade back and edge have identical curves, it can be a dagger shape if the back and edge are parallel, or a spear if the blade is widest where the point curve starts. There are numerous other blade shapes for your special needs, and variations include sheepsfoot and spey blades that see lots of use in pocket knives.

Most patterns are standard

Almost every knife company produces most of the standard patterns. A pocketknife maker will supply a Stockman's knife with clip, sheepsfoot and spey blades. The camper's model will have a large spear and shorter clip blade, along with a can opener, combination cap lifter and screwdriver, and an awl or punch—like those issued to members of the Swiss Army. The commercial versions of the Swiss Army knife go a lot further, and on some you can count a couple of dozen tools and gadgets.

Owners find constant use for such fold-out items as scissors, screwdriver (including a Phillips-head), saw, file, fishhook disgorger, inch and metric rules, can opener, miniature marlinespike and magnifying glass. More elaborate models also have tweezers and toothpick. There are lots of poor-imitation Swiss Army knives, but only two that have been made for over 80 years and are "official": the Victorinox, imported by Swiss Army Knives Inc., and Wenger, from Precise International.

Custom models

In spite of all the knives available, a lot of owners want one that's unique. Custom knifemakers fill this need, often at high prices and most of the time with superior quality. If a factory produces a pocketknife for $25, a lock-back for $50 and a straight blade hunter for $75, you usually can multiply those numbers by five or six for the price at custom makers.

You can also create your own custom knife with the help of knife parts suppliers. The do-it-yourself way to get started is to buy preground blades and put most of your effort into the handle. Shaping blades from raw bar stock and then properly hardening, tempering and polishing the steel takes a good deal of metalworking ability and access to advanced shop equipment.

You will learn that there's more to a knife than a blade and handle. A blade may have a back,

belly and sometimes a spine. The handle may be comprised of a guard, bolsters or pommel, along with scales. Underneath the handle of a fixed-blade knife is a tang. All these could be held together with solder, epoxy, cyanoacrylate adhesives, pins or cutlers' rivets.

Assessing value

You can probably produce an acceptable home-shop knife for about $20 or less, if you are buying supplies in quantity. Your knife is not likely to increase in value, but you will have the satisfaction of a hand-finished project. Nor do store-bought, factory-produced knives often increase in value. In spite of a few that have become collector's pieces, most are headed for useful work rather than glass cabinet. There are companies whose knives have a collector following.

Commemorative models

It's common for knife companies to produce commemorative models in limited quantities—instant collectors' pieces. Unfortunately for investors, it may take a couple of lifetimes for such knives to become more valuable. With hundreds of knife styles and millions of knives in annual production, it takes many years for a make or model to disappear so that a few can become rare. A limited edition knife may reach that rarity earlier, but most "limited editions" don't get used at all. If it's a 500-unit edition, there will be 500 around for a long time.

Price indicates quality

Knives are competitively priced—the market is too big to be otherwise—so the price of U.S. knives is usually a good indicator of quality in the knife you choose. As with most tools, buy the best you can afford for the job at hand. Look for top workmanship, or the lack of it, in the fit and finish. If an inspection of two similar knives doesn't show the difference, rely on price to indicate some hidden qualities or shortcuts. A high-priced knife *may* be cheaply made, but a cheap knife is *sure* to be.

Working from ladders

■ PROFESSIONAL LADDER-USERS will tell you, "If you don't know how to use a ladder wisely, you should stay on the ground." That advice is correct. Ladder accidents can be broken down into three groups:

- A ladder should have been replaced.
- The wrong kind of ladder for the job is used.
- A safe ladder is used improperly.

On these pages, you'll find all the know-how you need to avoid these common errors. And, for extra safety, *always* inspect a ladder before each use.

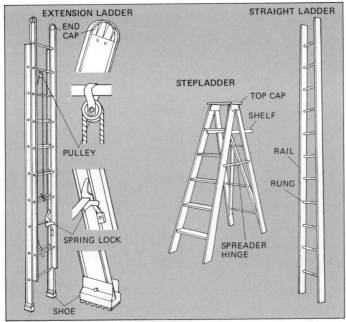

TYPICAL HOUSEHOLD LADDERS
Typical household stepladders come in 4, 5, 6 and 7-ft. heights. Taller ladders available are used mostly by pros. Single ladder is adequate if you own a ranch home, but for higher altitudes you'll need an extension ladder. These are available in wood, aluminum and magnesium.

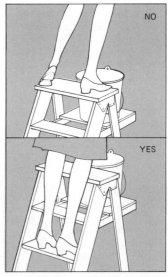

STEPLADDER SAFETY
Never stand on top cap (step) or tool shelf. If your shins rest against a tread, you have better balance and are working safely. Other tips: Always be sure that spreader hinges are fully locked, and, if you're working indoors on a dropcloth, smooth out the wrinkles before placing ladder.

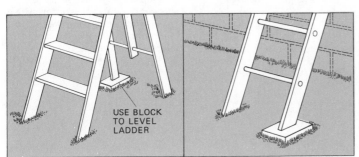

BE SURE LADDERS ARE LEVEL
Always "try" ladder on its first or second rung with a slight jump or bounce before climbing. This lets you know if the ladder is squarely planted or ground is too soggy. If either condition exists, use a board or ¾-in. plywood under one or both legs.

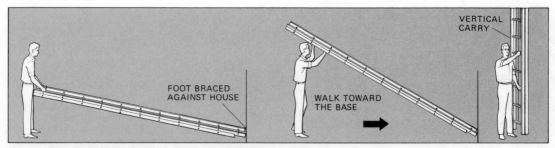

CARRYING AND ERECTING AN EXTENSION LADDER

To raise ladder, brace its foot against base of the house. Standing at opposite end, slowly walk toward base, transferring your hands from rung to rung as you go. (To lower ladder, reverse procedure.) To move ladder a short distance, carry it vertically after lowering top portion to maintain better control. If you're using an aluminum ladder, watch out for overhead power lines.

POSITIONING AND CLIMBING A LADDER

An extension ladder must be placed the correct distance from the wall it rests against. If the foot is too far out (sketch, top right), the base will slide away as you move your weight up the rungs; if too close, the ladder may tip backward or slide laterally on the wall. Overlap on an extension ladder is important, too; figure at least 3 ft. overlap for a 36-footer, 4 ft. for ladders up to 48 ft. and 5 ft. for longies up to 60 ft.

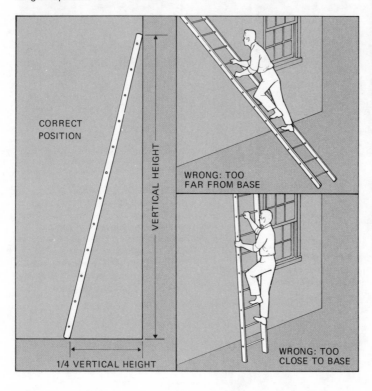

DON'T OVERREACH

Wrong way to work is shown in top drawing; this is uncomfortable and unsafe because user's weight is unevenly distributed, causing overload at one point. Right way to work is shown directly above. Set ladder where object to be painted (or worked) can be reached handily. Don't ever lean out far to one side of the ladder.

Long look at long ladders

■ LADDER SHOPPERS too hungry for a bargain risk getting tripped by cheap manufacturing and merchandising methods. In their scramble to undersell each other, many dealers search out ladders they can sell cheaply. At first glance, these rigs seem as good as those costing 25 percent or so more. But let's take a closer look.

The matter of length, for example, is trickier than you might think. A 24-foot extension ladder has two 12-foot sections—the "base" and the "fly" (see drawing). These long ladder sections should overlap 3 feet, giving you 21 feet of usable length. Sometimes, especially in cheaper ladders, this overlap is greater to increase rigidity. A tip-off here would be the location of the pulley. Normally, it would be on the top or second rung of the base. On a cheap ladder, the manufacturer may put it two or three rungs away to prevent

A COMMON WAY of fastening aluminum rungs into place in the side rails makes virtually a giant rivet of each rung. The collared rung goes into the rail (left) and is then peened over as shown in the cutaway section.

THE RUNGS of magnesium ladders are often welded in place (left). Before buying a ladder, try to twist each rung. They shouldn't budge. Photo at right shows a swivel mount for ladder feet; note the non-skid rubber "soles."

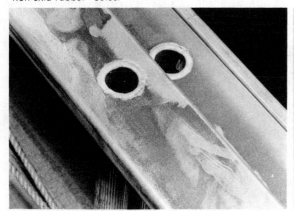

you from extending the ladder farther than is safe.

The best ladders have one rung per foot of nominal length. For instance, a 12-foot section of a 24-footer has 12 rungs, the lowest one 7 in. from the bottom, the top one 5 in. from the top. Cheaper ladders may have 11 rungs, starting up 1 ft. from the bottom and ending 1 ft. from the top. This is no great inconvenience, but it leaves 1 ft. of side rail at each end which is not supported by a rung. To reinforce the unsupported rails, some ladders may have a brace beneath the bottom rung. While the braces may give added strength, check to be sure they don't prevent maximum extension by interfering with the operation of the pulley.

Experts say that the longer a ladder is, the more you should pay for it, by the foot. One ladder-component manufacturer puts it this way: "The longer the side rails, the stronger they must be. The extra strength can come from only one thing—extra metal or wood."

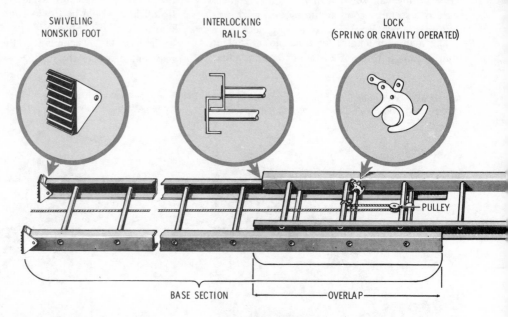

SWIVELING NONSKID FOOT — INTERLOCKING RAILS — LOCK (SPRING OR GRAVITY OPERATED) — PULLEY — BASE SECTION — OVERLAP

THE DRAWING ABOVE shows basic metal ladder assembly. Many will have rungs and feet shaped somewhat differently from the illustration. Some shorter models may have neither pulleys nor ropes.

THE CHART BELOW lists approximate specifications of well-made extension ladders. Height-in-place is less than nominal height because ladders are used at an angle and the sections overlap.

TYPICAL DIMENSIONS OF METAL EXTENSION LADDERS									
		Utility-household grade				Industrial-commercial grade			
NOMINAL HEIGHT	ACTUAL HEIGHT IN PLACE	WIDTH	CROSS SECTION OF RAIL	SIZE OF RUNG	WEIGHT	WIDTH	CROSS SECTION OF RAIL	SIZE OF RUNG	WEIGHT
16′	12′	15″	2½″x ¾″	1³⁄₁₆″	20 lbs	18-20″	3″x 1½″	1⁵⁄₁₆″	36 lbs
20′	16′	15″	2½″x ¾″	1³⁄₁₆″	25 lbs	18-20″	3″x 1½″	1⁵⁄₁₆″	44 lbs
24′	20′	15″	2½″x ¾″	1³⁄₁₆″	30 lbs	18-20″	3″x 1½″	1⁵⁄₁₆″	52 lbs
28′	24′	15″	2½″x ¾″	1³⁄₁₆″	35 lbs	18-20″	3″x 1½″	1⁵⁄₁₆″	59 lbs
32′	28′	15″	2½″x ¾″	1³⁄₁₆″	40 lbs	18-20″	3½″x 1½″	1⁵⁄₁₆″	73 lbs
36′	32′		Not recommended			18-20″	3½″x 1½″	1⁵⁄₁₆″	82 lbs
40′	34′		Not recommended			18-20″	3½″x 1½″	1⁵⁄₁₆″	90 lbs

Of course, there is nothing to keep someone from making a cheap 32-ft. ladder using rail stock meant for a 24-footer. As long as such a ladder is never twisted, never set up on uneven ground, never overloaded and never set up at too flat an angle everything may be fine and dandy. But the limitations easily cancel out the low price.

Weight per running foot

Metal ladder stock is graded by weight per running foot of rail. A good 24-footer may have rails that go .391 lbs. per foot. A higher ladder or a better 24-footer may go .440 lbs. per foot. Tops for homeowner equipment is around .550. It's hard to measure this weight on the dealer's floor, of course. All you can do is appraise the gauge of the metal by studying the ends of the rails. There are, in addition, two ways you can judge strength intelligently.

First, don't be so all-fired interested in lightness. Any good aluminum or magnesium rig is light enough. If it is too light, it may also be too weak for safety.

Second, here is an A.N.S.I. test for ladder rigidity: Extend the ladder to its permissible overlap. Place it flat on two supports spaced 6 in. from each end. Put a 2×4 or something similar across the ladder at midpoint and apply a 200-lb. load. The ladder must withstand the load without permanent bending or other visible weakening. Obviously, few dealers will let you perform this test on their merchandise. But it's worth a try.

Ladder experts agree that you should buy a ladder long enough to reach the highest point around your home. But, think twice about skinning up a 32- or 40-footer to reach the gable ends of a two-story house, especially if you're overweight, under-agile or inexperienced.

How wide should a ladder be? They generally run as narrow as 12 in., which is a bit skimpy. Good ones run 15 in. or more. A worthwhile industrial grade goes 20 in. Extra width, of course, provides greater stability and comfort for the user.

Incidentally, the once common practice of flaring the base section does little, if anything, for stability. It's impossible to flare the interlocking sections of a metal ladder, anyway, and the practice has even grown rare among wood-ladder makers.

Rungs and rails

Good rungs are important to quality. Wooden rungs should be pretty close to 1¼ in. in diame-

STRAIGHT GRAIN is important. This typical break followed the grain from edge to edge of the rail.

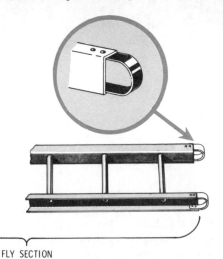

FLY SECTION

HEIGHT-TO-WEIGHT ratio is a guide to quality in stepladders and extensions. Ladders much lighter than indicated in the charts below and at left may have skimped on strength, stability and safety.

Stepladders: typical sizes and weights		
Light duty	3 feet	6 lbs
	4	9
	5	10½
	6	12
Utility	3 feet	7 lbs
	4	10
	5	11½
	6	14½
	7	18
	8	21
Industrial	4 feet	14 lbs
	5	16½
	6	20
	8	26½
	10	35
	12	42
	14	50

TO STIFFEN the side rails, the bottom two or three rungs of a metal stepladder, depending on its height, should have diagonal braces like these.

BOTH OF THESE wood ladders have straight grain, braced back section, and reinforcing rods under the rungs, but only one has non-skid rubber feet.

ter. Grain should be straight and clear. Edge grain should face the top of the ladder.

Metal rungs should be closed tubes which may be round or D-shaped, with the flat surface upward. Cheap ladders may have tubular rungs with open seams. A metal rung under $1\frac{3}{16}$ in. in diameter is too light. Good ladders usually have $1\frac{5}{16}$-in. rungs.

Some ladders have flat treads, riveted to the sides, or tubular rungs with flat treads welded on top. Both are more comfortable than plain rungs. The rivet construction, however, does not give the strength found in properly made round-rung ladders, and should, therefore, be reinforced with braces under several steps.

A ladder derives its basic strength from its side rails. In metal rigs, it's immaterial whether these are channel, I-beam, etc., as long as the metal is properly distributed between flanges and web. In simplest terms, the web provides the strength to keep the ladder from "bellying" when you stand on it. The flanges keep the ladder from bending sidewise. More critically, they hold the web in perfect plane, because the slightest bend or wave might let the web buckle.

Be suspicious of a side rail that measures less than $\frac{3}{4} \times 2\frac{1}{2}$ in. overall. Also, compare the dimensions with the weights in the chart mentioned previously, because a rail can be made with good dimensions, but with thin webs and flanges.

Hardware

Hardware varies greatly from ladder to ladder. Feet should swivel freely, to seat firmly on the ground. In some good ladders, they fasten to toothed projections. In icy conditions, you remove the rubber-soled feet and let the teeth take over. Locks may be gravity-operated or spring-loaded. In either case, try them out. If they are tricky or temperamental, the fly section might crash down unexpectedly as you raise or lower it.

Some metal ladders have little wheels at the top to facilitate raising and lowering of the fly. Make sure such wheels are solidly made. An alternative to wheels is skids, usually in the form of an arch over the top of each rail or a curved nosing at the end of each rail. Sometimes these are covered with plastic to keep aluminum from marking the side of the house. Magnesium doesn't mark, needs no such cover.

So far, we've talked mostly about metal extension ladders. What's the story on metal vs. wood? Essentially, wood ladders cost less and weigh more.

Check side rail quality

In judging the quality of a wooden ladder, look for side rails of straight-grained fir, hemlock, pine or spruce. Spruce is best, but getting scarce. The edge of the grain must fall on the edge of the rail. Ash or oak (especially red or scrub oak) make the best rungs. There are probably fewer bad wooden ladders on the market than bad metal ones, since there is less price competition.

Is wood safer than metal around high-voltage wires? Well, it is true that you can electrocute yourself by touching a metal ladder to a high-voltage wire, but the antidote is to avoid the wires, not the metal ladders.

Which brings us to stepladders. There has been considerable effort by manufacturers to reduce weights in this group. That should, after all, make their product more appealing to their customers. But the result is that many stepladders on the market today are virtually worthless—or even dangerous to use. Light weight can hardly be that important.

Actually, the vast majority of light around-the-house jobs can best be handled from a 24- or 27-in. step stool.

The back rails of a good metal stepladder are usually made of channel. Angle can be adequate, however, if the rails are heavy enough. In many cases, you'll find X-bracing between the rear rails, for rigidity, but some products have rungs you could stand on in a pinch. The X-brace breaks up the geometry into triangles—the strongest and most rigid form possible, so the best models have X-bracing as well as rungs.

When you're sizing up a stepladder, open it up and flip down the pail shelf. Then pull down on it. The A.N.S.I. says it should be able to handle a 50-lb. load without failing. And don't be hesitant about checking it out thoroughly; if the retailer isn't confident enough in the merchandise to let you test it, you're better off to get your ladder someplace else. After all, the few bucks you might save with a "bargain" can hardly compensate you for the pain and financial cost of injuries from a ladder that can't handle the job.

The ladder's overall dimensions indicate a lot about its stability. Further, they can help you recognize the product of a manufacturer that has tried to cut corners a bit here and there.

Start with the profile

Start out with a look at the ladder's profile. Unless it was especially designed for working unusually close to a wall (a technique that demands special care and is usually better left to professionals), it should follow a minimum spread proportion: The front and back should spread about 5½ in. farther apart for each foot of height. Thus the rear feet should be nearly 36 in. from the front ones for a 6-ft. ladder. The proportion should be even greater for short ladders, to insure enough stability.

Now take a head-on look. The ladder should be at least 1 ft. wide at the top, and each side should spread away from vertical at the rate of an inch per foot. Thus, a 6-footer will spread to around 24 in. at the base. Again, the degree of splay is greater for short ladders.

Special purpose stepladders

Finally, a word about a few special-purpose stepladders. At least one—the platform type—is often more comfortable than the standard variety. It has a platform near the top for you to stand on. Such ladders are classified by height. A "No. 8," for example, will be around 8 ft. high, with the platform about 6 ft. from the ground when in use.

The double-front, or trestle, ladder has two fronts instead of a front and back, permitting two people to stand on it simultaneously. Such models are usually strong and stable, and prove handy for such jobs as applying gypsum board to a ceiling.

As you can imagine, there aren't many instances when you'll need this extra versatility. Since there is little call for a double-front ladder in the do-it-yourself market, these are usually available only in commercial or industrial grades. The extra convenience is rather costly.

Lamps and lighting

■ HOME LIGHTING IS produced by three systems: incandescent, fluorescent, and HID (high-intensity discharge). The bulbs and fixtures for these types cannot be mixed.

Incandescent lighting. Incandescent lighting is produced by a bulb with glowing tungsten filaments—the familiar type invented by Thomas Edison a century ago. Styles of incandescent fixtures are seemingly limitless; they can be mounted directly to a ceiling or wall box or plugged into a receptacle. Or the fixtures may be recessed, on a track or pendant-type. Portable lamps (those that sit on tables, dressers, desks, etc.) have a bulb socket made of brass. The sockets are connected to standard No. 18 lamp cord, and the end of the cord has a plug for a receptacle. The parts—sockets, insulation, housing, plugs—are standard and may be replaced individually.

Track lighting. Track lighting systems use incandescent fixtures that slide on open or closed channel tracks fastened to the ceiling with screws, toggle or Molly bolts in almost any configuration you want. The tracks are usually wired to a ceiling box for power.

The power flows through a metal strip in the tracks. The fixtures plug into and slide along the track. Open tracks let you set the lights anywhere you want by simply sliding the light along the tracks. Closed-channel tracks position the light fixtures more or less permanently in one position.

Some types of track lighting don't have to be connected to a ceiling box; they use a cord and plug combination that is plugged into a regular wall receptacle. Also available are fittings that let you connect track lights to the grid system of suspended ceilings, along with T, X and L junctions to direct the track anywhere in the room.

Fluorescent lighting. Because it takes less power to operate, fluorescent lighting is a bargain. The fixtures themselves, however, cost as much as incandescent fixtures. There is a variety of fluorescent fixture styles, sizes and shapes: strip lights, under-cabinet lights, round lamps and units that are recessed in ceilings, under soffits, behind valances and in suspended ceilings.

Fluorescent fixtures are connected to ceiling or wall junction boxes; some models have power cords that are plugged into regular house power outlets; still others are screwed into light sockets. The junction-box mounting technique, however, is the most popular.

The parts of a fluorescent fixture include the metal housing, ballast (a kind of transformer), lamp starters, lamp holders and lamp tube. All are replaceable separately. To buy a replacement part, you must first know what part is malfunctioning. The following explanation of fluorescent light faults will help you diagnose the trouble and know what to fix.

No light: If the fixture is receiving power, first check the electrical connections—the lamp holders and the wire connections from the ceiling box to the ballast hook-up. If these aren't the problem, replace the starter, tube and ballast, in that order.

Light is partially on: Replace the starter; if this fails, replace the tubes.

OUTDOOR SECURITY LIGHTS are energy-efficient, and some have photoelectric switches for automatic dawn-to-dusk protection.

LOW-COST fluorescent fixture sticks under cabinets with self-adhering tape, providing light for work areas without running new wiring.

Light flickers: Try reseating the starter. Then try reseating the tube. If the light is new, it may flicker for an hour or two. If the light is old, it may flicker just before it burns out. Any light may flicker if the temperature in the room is below 50°F.

Hum: Go right to the ballast. The connections are probably loose. If not, replace the ballast.

HID lighting fixtures. HID lighting is generated by mercury-vapor, sodium-vapor or metal halide devices. The fixtures have a ballast similar to a fluorescent unit. Flood and spot lighting are available. The lights range in wattages from 50 to 1500; they are generally cheaper to operate than incandescent lights, and the bulbs last longer than incandescents.

For the most part, HID lighting is used outdoors to flood a landscape at night with light or to spotlight a yard feature such as a beautiful tree or garden or swimming pool.

Low-voltage lighting. Low-voltage lighting uses a transformer to reduce regular house power to 6 or 10 volts, to operate doorbells or small outdoor lights.

The system usually is sold in kit form, although you can buy separate components to assemble them; you can make kit repairs with separate components. Bell cord is used to distribute power from the transformer to the lights,

THIS FLUORESCENT light bulb replacement provides a table lamp with light at a fraction of the cost of an ordinary bulb.

which are clipped to the cords without special connections, junction boxes or splicing. The bulbs are 25- and 50-watt size. The basic hook-up is simply plugging the transformer into a regular house power circuit.

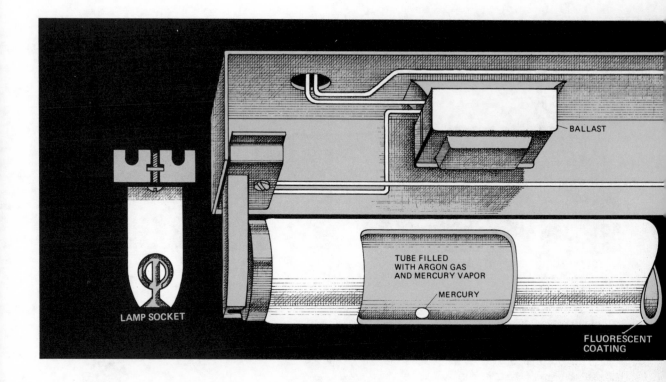

BALLAST

TUBE FILLED
WITH ARGON GAS
AND MERCURY VAPOR

MERCURY

LAMP SOCKET

FLUORESCENT
COATING

Fluorescent lamp basics

■ THE FACT THAT IT saves energy—as well as money—makes fluorescence an increasingly popular alternative to incandescence in office and home. Energy-saving fluorescent lamps give two to four times as much light per watt of power as incandescent bulbs. They also have low surface brightness. Unlike incandescent lamps, which are bright in just a single spot, fluorescents have a lower brightness over a larger area, resulting in fewer shadows, less eyestrain and better distribution.

Tubular in form, fluorescent lamps are usually called tubes and come in straight and circular styles. Straight fluorescents vary in length from 4¼ to 96 in. and from 4 to 215 watts. Circular fluorescents are available in outside diameters of 8¼, 12 and 16 in. with popular powers of 22, 32 and 40 watts.

The ends of each tube contain a cap with two terminals. These terminals connect to an internal tungsten filament inside each end of the tube. Inside the tube is a small amount of argon gas and a drop of mercury; the inside surface is coated with a fluorescent chemical.

In addition to the tube, the circuit contains a switch, ballast (transformer) and starter. A pull-chain toggle or pushbutton switch turns the circuit on and off. The ballast provides the high voltage necessary to start the mercury-vapor arc inside the tube and stabilizes the circuit by keeping the operating current at a steady value, as shown in the two-lamp circuit diagram.

The starting switch closes the circuit between the two filaments when the lamp circuit is energized. It also opens the circuit between the two filaments after sufficient time has passed to heat

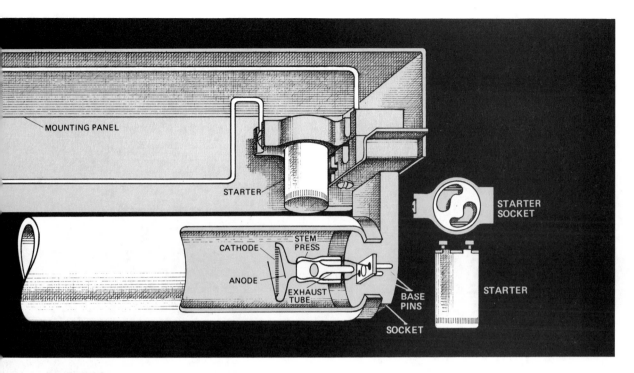

MOUNTING PANEL

STARTER

CATHODE

STEM PRESS

ANODE

EXHAUST TUBE

BASE PINS

SOCKET

STARTER SOCKET

STARTER

Blackening

POSSIBLE CAUSES	WHAT TO TRY
1. Mercury deposit inside of tube.	Normal.
2. Lamp failure.	Replace lamp.
3. Frequent starting.	Limit number of times lamp is turned on and off. Allow three to four hours of lamp operation.
4. Wrong-size ballast.	Check fluorescent specifications.
5. Low line voltage.	See "Lamp slow in starting."

Swirling and spiraling inside of lamp

POSSIBLE CAUSES	WHAT TO TRY
1. Lamp failure.	Replace lamp.
2. Improper or defective starter.	Check starter against fluorescent lamp circuit specifications. Replace defective starter.
3. Wrong-size ballast.	Check fluorescent specifications.
4. Low line voltage.	See "Lamp slow in starting."

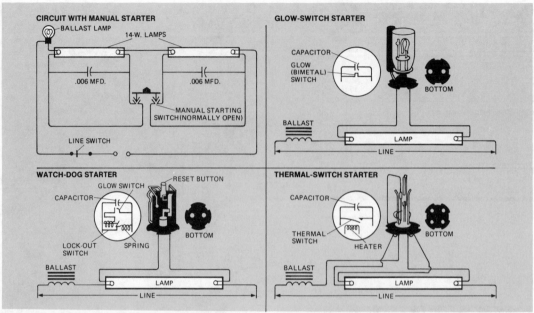

FOUR DIFFERENT STARTER CIRCUITS available for fluorescent lamps are shown. When you "turn on" a lamp by throwing a line switch, the circuit is closed, but the light does not appear immediately.

THE JOB OF THE STARTER ELEMENT is to hold up the flow of electrical current until it has heated the two filaments in each lamp on the circuit to their proper temperature. The delay may take a second.

LAMP WATT/LENGTH RATIO	
Watts	Length (in.)
15	18
20	24
30	36
40	48
100	60

the filaments to the proper temperature. There are four different starter circuits available: manual, automatic glow-switch, automatic watch-dog and automatic thermal-switch.

A circuit for a fluorescent tube shows a ballast connected in series with the lamp. The automatic starter switch is in closed position when no current is flowing through the circuit, though the starter element is heating (diagram A, "Glow-switch operation"). When the circuit is closed (diagram B), the two lamp filaments are connected in series through the starter to supply voltage. Since the automatic starter short-circuits the path, no current will flow in the lamp. Thus, the filaments are cold, and argon gas cannot conduct.

As the current begins to heat the lamp filaments to a certain temperature, the mercury in the lamp begins to vaporize. A few seconds later, the automatic starter opens (diagram C), breaks

the circuit and causes the ballast to produce high voltage between the filaments. This voltage strikes an arc through the argon gas and mercury vapor. The mercury-vapor arc then causes the fluorescent chemicals inside the tube to fluoresce, emitting a brilliant light which illuminates the lamp.

Fluorescent lamps are available in many colors and "whites." Colors are used for decorative purposes; whites for general lighting. These whites offer the most efficiency per dollar of cost, the best color-rendering per-dollar cost, the best color-rendering properties.

The life of fluorescent lamps is not only affected by voltage and current, but also by the number of times they are started. Homeowners can prolong this life by following these suggestions:

● Operate lamps continuously for a three to four-hour period for maximum life. Turning the lamp on and off cuts its life considerably.

● Room temperature should be at least 50° F. For colder rooms, special fluorescent lamps and starters can be used.

● The right starter should be used with fluorescents. Check replacement starter numbers against numbers stamped on the original starter.

● Be sure the ballast has the catalog or type number specified for the fluorescent lamp unit.

Ends of lamp remain lighted

POSSIBLE CAUSES	WHAT TO TRY
1. Shorted starter.	Replace starter.
2. Lamp failure.	Replace lamp.
3. Incorrect wiring.	Check wiring against manufacturer's schematic.

BASIC SINGLE-LAMP CIRCUIT

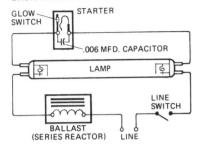

Lamp does not start

POSSIBLE CAUSES	WHAT TO TRY
1. Lamp not seated in sockets.	Reseat lamps firmly in sockets.
2. Defective starter.	Replace starter.
3. Defective lamp.	Replace lamp.
4. Defective switch.	Disconnect power. Place a continuity tester across switch. Turn switch on. A reading should exist. If not, replace switch.
5. Defective ballast.	If all of the above check out, then replace the ballast.

GLOW-SWITCH OPERATION

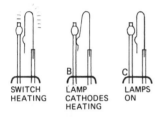

Lamp slow in starting

POSSIBLE CAUSES	WHAT TO TRY
1. Defective starter.	Replace starter.
2. Wrong-size ballast.	Check fluorescent specifications.
3. Low line voltage.	Check voltage. It must be ±10 percent of 120 v. If not, check with power company.

SINGLE-LAMP CIRCUIT WITH AUTOTRANSFORMER BALLAST

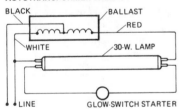

Lamp blinks on and off

POSSIBLE CAUSES	WHAT TO TRY
1. Lamp failure.	Replace lamp.
2. Defective starter.	Replace starter.
3. Cold drafts or low temperature.	Block drafts or heat room up to above 50°F.
4. Wrong-size ballast.	Refer to previous section.
5. Low line voltage.	Refer to previous section.

TWO-LAMP CIRCUIT

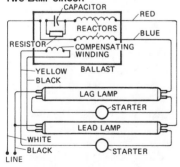

Low-energy lighting saves money

■ WHERE CAN YOU BUY more for less these days? One bright answer rests with new lighting products, where you can find a better deal than putting your money into standard incandescent bulbs.

Here's a quick rundown on the advantages of these new products (though not all deliver all the advantages).

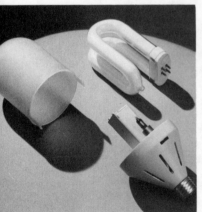

A TOUGH ACRYLIC cover wraps this fluorescent and its compact, instant ballast. The cover fits as handily as an incandescent bulb into a globe fixture.

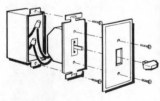

SODIUM OUTDOOR light spreads bright yellow light for one-quarter acre. It features low energy use.

EASILY INSTALLED dimmer is made to work on incandescents.

• You gain more light for less money.
• These sources deliver illumination over a longer period of time—sometimes over 25 times as long, and are therefore more convenient to use.
• With new sources in place, the electric meter spins more slowly.

If all this is true, why isn't everyone rushing out to buy? For three reasons: 1. The initial cost is higher than what you pay now for standard incandescent bulbs; 2. for pin-contact fluorescent tubes, you may have to buy a fixture as well; 3. it's likely you'll have to search beyond the supermarket to locate the right "color" fluorescent tubes or one of the newer, energy-saving offerings described here.

Table-lamp fluorescents

Now you can simply toss out a spent incandescent bulb from that end-table lamp and screw in a fluorescent. Illumination is every bit as good using a fluorescent—if not better. You're also due cash savings in two ways: There's less draw on your electricity with a fluorescent; its long life will cut your bulb bill.

Fluorescence demands only a small amount of electric power before it's aglow. For example, in a year-long comparison, assuming lights are on in the house for about five hours a day (roughly normal), Duro-Lite matches one 40-watt Vita-Lite fluorescent against two 75-watt incandescents. Over the 365 days of our test, the two incandescents burned up $16.43 worth of energy, while the fluorescent consumed a mere $4.38—both figures based on a moderate rate of 6 cents per kwh. Your costs now may differ from those we incurred during the test.

In this example, there's a bonus. The two bulbs, burning at a 150-watt rate, produce 1,980 lumens (standard measure of light output). The 40-watt fluorescent tube delivers 2,180 lumens.

(Note: A 40-watt fluorescent in use actually draws 54 watts, the difference made up by electricity demand for the ballast—a device that controls voltage, wave pattern and current delivered to the vapor within the near-vacuum tube. The $4.38 figure above is based on 54 watts.)

During the same year's period, a number of incandescents (note plural) will cost more than a fluorescent (note singular). How much more? Lithonia Lighting did a study based on 1980 retail prices. Two 60-watt incandescent bulbs were tagged at $1.62, while a lumen-equivalent circular fluorescent of 32 watts (35-watt total with ballast) was $8.85.

During the year those incandescents kept burning out. Replacements ran up a bill of $17.82. The fluorescent continued to work. As with the Duro-Lite test, figures were based on average home use of light. The final score: incandescents—$19.44; fluorescent—$8.85, a saving of $10.59.

At the heart of the new table-lamp fluorescents is a redesigned ballast, small enough to screw into the existing socket. Over the ballast shaft slides the fluorescent unit. Once in place and re-shaded, the lamp operates the same. The difference: The light just lasts and lasts.

Three major producers, General Electric, Sylvania and Westinghouse, have introduced table-lamp fluorescents. GE and Sylvania offer an adaptation of the circular fluorescent introduced in the 1940s (and still available), a dinner-plate-diameter tube that often found its way to the kitchen ceiling. Westinghouse developed a U-shaped, mini-fluorescent packed into a tube not vastly different from an incandescent bulb.

For three-way fixtures, GE offers a two-way fluorescent delivering the brightness level of a 50-watt and 100-watt incandescent, but doing it on 16 and 44 watts. The company also produces similar units at one-level brightnesses of 60 watts (actual 22 watts), and 100 watts (actual 44 watts). At 22 watts, Sylvania's entry puts out 75-watt brightness and Westinghouse's small tube throws out light of 60 to 75 watts on a demand of 27 watts.

One of these five new fluorescents ought to fit just about any standard-size socket in your home, including wall sconces and ceiling fixtures. Replacing every bulb in an average three-bedroom house could bring year-end savings of $200 to $400.

Read the fine print, though. For example, GE warns you not to close in its two-way tube with a frosted glass-covered ceiling fixture or globe-shaped swag light. Heat buildup within the confined space could knock out the tube.

A subtler reason than inconvenience has kept fluorescents out of living areas for years. "Colors look crazy under that light," say many who have tried them. This is partly true. Under the harsh light of cool white fluorescents, a bright fire-engine-red pillow could look almost gray. People tend to look wan and unhealthy.

LOW-WATT FLUORESCENTS placed under kitchen cabinets serve as security lights as shown above.

BUILT-IN DOWNLIGHTS reflect off glass and a mirror back into the room.

Soft white fluorescents

Unfortunately, not many know there are more "colors" than cool white. Recognizing the problem, all three makers produce table-lamp fluorescents in a "soft white" rendering, which makes clothes, food and you look more the way you expect.

Yet the cool-white conventional unit remains for anyone wishing to buy fluorescent tubes in 20-, 30-, or 40-watt sizes. Savings easily equal, and sometimes exceed, those you reap with the new table-lamp units. Fixture makers have also designed attractive new covers for ceiling-mounted fluorescents.

Manufacturers of incandescents are also redesigning for efficiency. From GE and Westinghouse come three-way bulbs at 15/135/150 watts, replacing the conventional 50/100/150 watts. The concept: Who needs 50 watts for conversation, 'watching TV, or as a security light when 15 watts will do? Because of a redesigned tungsten coil, the 135-watt setting produces 8 percent more light than the 150-watt level on the older bulb.

Need a close-up light for shop, study or as an accent on a piece of art? GE recently introduced a watt-saving reflector bulb. This 50-watter is housed in its own swivel fixture for around $11. Because the light is concentrated, the subject is illuminated as much as it would be by a standard 100-watt bulb.

Sylvania has joined the energy-saving clan with four bulbs at slightly less wattages than standard. For example, it offers a 69-watter to do the work of an ordinary 75-watt bulb.

Floodlamps for outdoor safety and security are effective, but they eat up energy dollars.

Sodium lights

However, Norelco offers a low-pressure sodium light that will economically illuminate up to one-quarter acre, or 10,000 sq. ft. There is a yellow cast to the light, but if safety and security are concerns, this fixture is a good investment.

Light dimmers help you chip away at your electric bill and lengthen bulb life. Incandescent light dimmers are simple to install. One type replaces a wall switch; another cuts into a fixture cord and a third kind wires to an existing table lamp. Prices are $5 to about $25.

Fluorescent dimmers work only on standard 30 to 40-watt, rapid-start fluorescent tubes. In addition, each tube must have a special ballast to replace the original one. Price of the ballast: about $30. The dimmer, which costs $40 to $50, works on one or up to 30 fluorescents.

Savings do accrue using any dimmer. Suppose you consistently burn a 100-watt incandescent at 70-percent capacity. That results in a 17.5-percent saving in electricity.

Common sense suggests other ways to trim your bills; for example, dining by candlelight and chatting by firelight. What could be nicer?

Spanish-style lamp

THE MEDITERRANEAN lamp's handsome appearance belies its origin as a quick weekend project.

■ WHY SPEND a lot of money for an imported Mediterranean table lamp, with its customary heavy, large-scale wood base, when you can build this beauty for a fraction of the price in an evening or two?

The lamp's construction is greatly simplified by the use of ready-made spindles. They're available in a variety of styles and sizes at lumberyards and most well-stocked hardware stores.

Begin the project by lining up, measuring and cutting the spindles to desired length. Overall length is not critical; determine it so that it places the lamp at the proper height for the place you want to use it. All four spindles must be the same length.

Because it will be impossible to get inside the column once it is assembled, each spindle should be stained before assembly. Do *not* stain those surfaces which will mate and receive glue. If you use a hot-melt glue gun, assembly is speeded up. If you use white glue, it will be necessary, of course, to clamp the pieces overnight before proceeding with the slats and electrical work. The base-surround (slats) is made up of ¼ x 1⅛-in. lattice strips. And once these are added, the lamp should be freestanding. If the lamp wobbles, true up the bottom with a block of wood covered with coarse-grit sandpaper. Dowel buttons were used for accent but, if preferred, roundhead tacks can be substituted. For rustic effect and a more Spanish-looking appearance, these buttons can be painted black.

Drill a ¼-in. hole through the top and bottom of the lamp to receive the lamp cord. Also, for the cord, cut a small half-circle channel in the bottom from the hole to one edge of the base. A pipe flange (painted black) goes at the top of the lamp and you're all ready for the electrical part of the job. Lampshades can be found in department stores; This permits selecting a color and pattern that will blend with your own room decor.

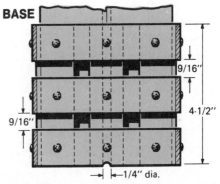

BASE

9/16"

9/16"

4-1/2"

1/4" dia.

THE OVERALL SIZE of the base is governed by the size of the spindles you choose to buy.

THE SPINDLES are lined up and cut to length. A planer blade will eliminate much sanding.

DRILL HOLES through the centers of the top and the base of the column. Use a ¼-in. drill bit.

A PIPE FLANGE is centered on top of the column. Mark and punch pilot holes but do not fasten.

VERTICAL SLATS on the base are placed and glued. Measuring isn't necessary; space them by eye.

HORIZONTAL SLATS can be affixed with a hot-melt glue gun (shown parked in a discarded aerosol can cover).

TURNED PARTS can be finished while in the lathe. After turning is completed, sand glass-smooth with extra-fine paper and apply colonial oil stain. Finally, polish with wax and soft cloth while the work is actually spinning.

Candlestand lamp

■ IF YOUR LATHE has become a forgotten tool, maybe it's time to dust it off, oil it up and once again enjoy the fun of watching a spinning chunk of wood turn into a pleasing shape before your eyes.

To start you off again on a lathe project, we built this charming colonial candlestand lamp and photographed it in a true early American setting. Made entirely of cherry, it has the warmth of colonial furniture. Graceful scrolls of black wrought iron add a distinctive touch to its three-legged base.

While a lathe plays a major part in making this lamp, your bandsaw, router and drill press won't stand idly by—you'll need them for making the base and circular table.

The base consists of three identical parts, bandsawed from 1½-in. stock and butt-glued at the center. The top and bottom edges are rounded with a ¼-round bit in your router. Finally, a 1-in. hole is bored all the way through the base at the center.

Rough turning squares for the upper and lower posts are glued up from two dadoed pieces to form a square hole their full lengths for the ⅛-in. running-threaded pipe.

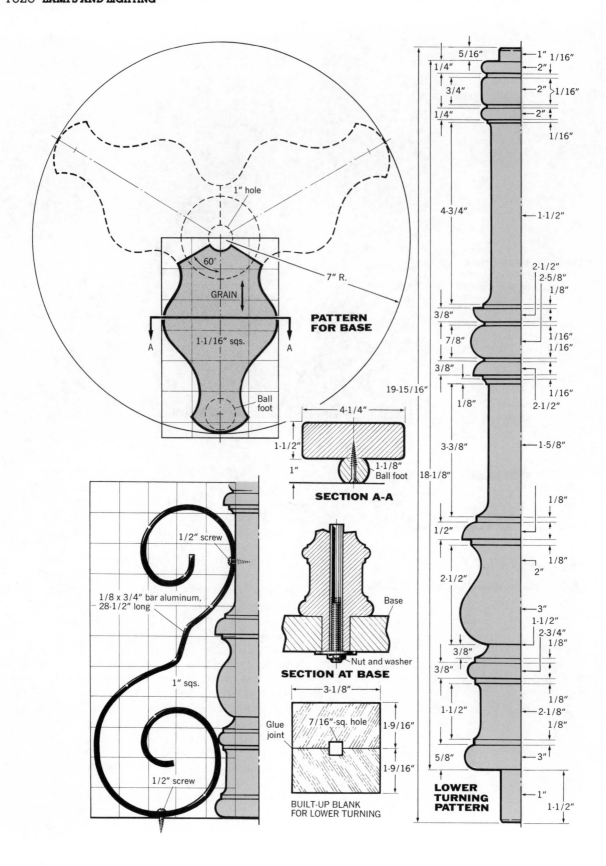

PATTERN FOR BASE

60°

GRAIN

1" hole

7" R.

1-1/16" sqs.

A — A

Ball foot

SECTION A-A

4-1/4"

1-1/2"

1"

1-1/8"
Ball foot

19-15/16"

18-1/8"

SECTION AT BASE

1/2" screw

1/8 x 3/4" bar aluminum,
28-1/2" long

1" sqs.

1/2" screw

Base

Nut and washer

Glue joint

7/16"-sq. hole

3-1/8"

1-9/16"

1-9/16"

**BUILT-UP BLANK
FOR LOWER TURNING**

**LOWER
TURNING
PATTERN**

5/16"

1/4"

3/4"

1/4"

1" 1/16"

2"

2" 1/16"

2"

1/16"

4-3/4"

1-1/2"

2-1/2"
2-5/8"
1/8"

3/8"

7/8"

1/16"
1/16"

3/8"

1/8"

1/16"

2-1/2"

3-3/8"

1-5/8"

1/8"

1/2"

1/8"

2-1/2"

2"

3"
1-1/2"
2-3/4"
1/8"

3/8"

3/8"

1/8"

1-1/2"

2-1/8"
1/8"

5/8"

3"

1"

1-1/2"

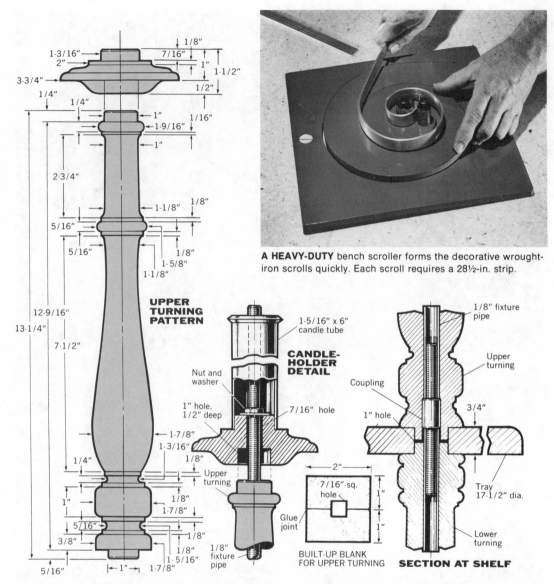

UPPER TURNING PATTERN

A HEAVY-DUTY bench scroller forms the decorative wrought-iron scrolls quickly. Each scroll requires a 28½-in. strip.

CANDLE-HOLDER DETAIL

1-5/16" x 6" candle tube

Nut and washer

1" hole, 1/2" deep

7/16" hole

Upper turning

1/8" fixture pipe

Glue joint

7/16"-sq. hole

2"

BUILT-UP BLANK FOR UPPER TURNING

1/8" fixture pipe

Upper turning

Coupling

1" hole

3/4"

Tray 17-1/2" dia.

Lower turning

SECTION AT SHELF

While you only need to turn one of each post, you'll find it easier to work from a full-size pattern from which you can take divider and caliper measurements directly. Notice that 1-in. tenons are turned on each end of both turnings, the longest one being that which passes through the hole in the base.

Since you cannot buy ⅛-in. threaded pipe in lengths longer than 36 in., two lengths are joined with a coupling. To accommodate the coupling, the square hole in the upper turning must be drilled larger for a distance of 2 in.

The tenons on the upper and lower turnings meet midway in the hole in the table. A slight clearance between the two tenons will assure a tight fit when all the parts are later pulled to-gether by a nut and washer at the bottom of the pipe.

The candleholder is faceplate-turned to fit over the tenon at the top of the upper turning. Notice that it has a tenon for a 6-in. length of cardboard candle tubing. The brass cap which fits on top of the tubing is a standard lamp fitting. The ⅛-in. pipe should extend about ¼ in. above the cap for a harp, socket and 14-in. linen shade.

The three wrought-iron scrolls are formed from ⅛ x ¾-in. aluminum bar, drilled for ½-in. roundhead wood screws and then sprayed flat black. You'll need to enlarge the pattern and use it as a guide. Three ball feet, flattened top and bottom for attaching with flathead wood screws, are painted flat black to complete the lamp.

Cobbler's bench table lamp

■ WHEN YOUR FRIENDS see this charming little table lamp, you won't stop with one—you'll wind up making several. Made in the form of an old cobbler's bench from scraps of clear white pine, the lamp is more than just a lamp. It has a rack for letters to be mailed, a handly little drawer for stamps and a place for a live or artificial plant.

It's a project you can quickly mass-produce with workshop tools. The straight and slanting grooves for the letter rack can be run on your table saw. The 15° holes for the legs can be bored uniformly with a simple jig clamped to your drill press. The flowerpot hole can be cut neatly with a hole cutter, and the hole through the square tapered lamppost can be bored from each end with a ¼-in. wood bit. The upper end of the post is counterbored for a 2-in. length of ⅛-in. fixture pipe turned tightly into an undersize hole. The lower end is whittled round to fit a ⅞-hole. A standard brass pushbutton socket is screwed onto the pipe.

To produce an antique look, round off all sharp edges with fine sandpaper and distress the wood by sanding worn spots at points which would receive wear, like the seat, the drawer front and the letter rack, always sanding with the grain. Then go over the whole thing and "polish" the wood with a worn piece of extra fine sandpaper.

Coat the wood with a brown pigmented wiping stain, let flatten, then wipe off, leaving it heavier in the corners and imperfections. When the stain is semidry, dip a cloth pad in turpentine and add highlights here and there by deftly wiping away some of the stain at the worn spots, the cheeks of the legs, the drawer pull and other places. Let dry overnight, then apply three coats of self-rubbing polyurethane varnish, sanding lightly between coats. Complete by wiring the socket.

GROOVES in the drawer slide on L-shaped runners. Fit the socket with a 40-w. bulb and 10-in. shade.

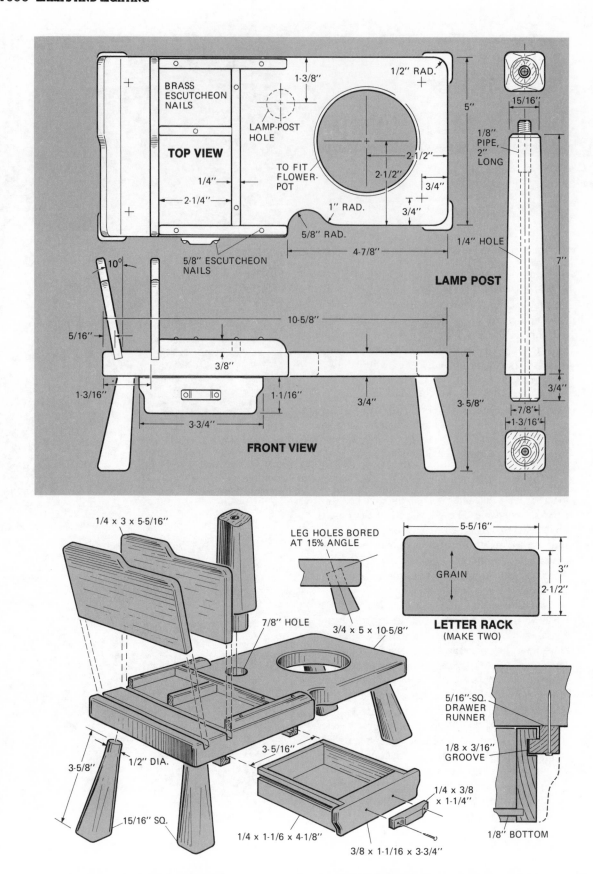

BRASS ESCUTCHEON NAILS

TOP VIEW

LAMP-POST HOLE

TO FIT FLOWER-POT

1-3/8"

1/2" RAD.

5"

2-1/2"

2-1/2"

3/4"

1/4"

2-1/4"

1" RAD.

5/8" RAD.

5/8" ESCUTCHEON NAILS

4-7/8"

3/4"

3/4"

15/16"

1/8" PIPE, 2" LONG

1/4" HOLE

LAMP POST

7"

3/4"

7/8"

1-3/16"

10°

5/16"

10-5/8"

3/8"

1-3/16"

3-3/4"

1-1/16"

3/4"

3-5/8"

FRONT VIEW

1/4 x 3 x 5-5/16"

LEG HOLES BORED AT 15% ANGLE

5-5/16"

GRAIN

3"

2-1/2"

LETTER RACK
(MAKE TWO)

7/8" HOLE

3/4 x 5 x 10-5/8"

3-5/16"

1/2" DIA.

3-5/8"

15/16" SQ.

5/16"-SQ. DRAWER RUNNER

1/8 x 3/16" GROOVE

1/8" BOTTOM

1/4 x 3/8 x 1-1/4"

1/4 x 1-1/6 x 4-1/8"

3/8 x 1-1/16 x 3-3/4"

Six-in-one wood lamp

■ CAREFUL ATTENTION to construction detail makes this lamp give the illusion that it has been carved from a single block of wood. Actually, it consists of six separate wood members. The lamp shown is of walnut with the legs requiring ¾-in. material, the center blocks 2-in. turning-square stock, and the base a 2x10-in. turning block. You will also need a 2-ft. length of ½-in.-dia. brass tubing.

To start, make a full-size paper or cardboard template of a typical leg section using the dimensions shown. Lay out the three legs on the ¾-in. stock and cut to rough contour shape and sand. Next, make a template of the center-block end view and cut these two parts. But before cutting the center blocks, drill a ½-in.-dia. hole through the exact center of both to receive the tubing that houses wiring.

Next, cut the 2-in. base stocks to 9¼-in.-dia. disc. Drill a ½-in.-dia. hole ¾ in. deep in the top of the base to accommodate the brass tube. Then, continue drilling through the base with a ¼-in. drill. Enlarge the hole, from the bottom up, to ⅝-in.-dia. and a depth of ⅝ in. Finally, turn the base to finished shape.

After you sand all wood parts, the base is ready for assembly. Lay a piece of wood across the shaped portion of the center block to serve as

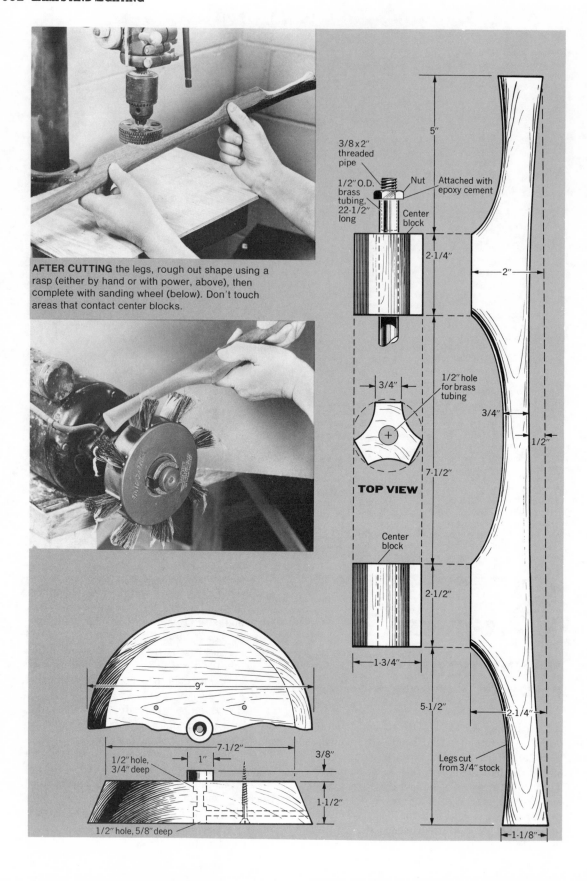

AFTER CUTTING the legs, rough out shape using a rasp (either by hand or with power, above), then complete with sanding wheel (below). Don't touch areas that contact center blocks.

3/8 x 2″ threaded pipe

1/2″ O.D. brass tubing, 22-1/2″ long

Nut

Attached with epoxy cement

Center block

5″

2-1/4″

2″

3/4″

3/4″

1/2″

1/2″ hole for brass tubing

7-1/2″

TOP VIEW

Center block

2-1/2″

1-3/4″

5-1/2″

2-1/4″

Legs cut from 3/4″ stock

9″

7-1/2″

1″

3/8″

1/2″ hole, 3/4″ deep

1-1/2″

1/2″ hole, 5/8″ deep

1-1/8″

a support for clamping. Glue one flat portion of each block to one leg, clamp and allow to dry. Then glue and clamp the second and third legs.

Cut the ½-in. tubing to an overall length of 22½ in. Then cut a length of ⅛-in. running-thread fixture pipe (⅜-in. O.D.) 2 in. long. Turn on a brass hex nut until the pipe protrudes ¼ in. above it. Fit the longer length of the pipe inside the brass tube and glue the nut to the tube with epoxy cement. Slip the brass tubing through center holes of the leg assembly and push the tube

into the "collar" in the base. Drill holes through the base up into each leg and secure with screws.

The cord is threaded through the hole on the base edge and pulled out the bottom hole. After double-looping the end, thread the cord back up through the hole and brass tube until it comes out the top. Attach the cord to a push-through-type socket and pull the cord back down to screw the socket to the threaded pipe above the hex nut.

Finish the piece as desired; it goes a lot faster if done before final assembly.

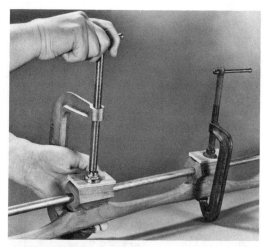

SLIP BRASS TUBE through holes in center blocks, glue blocks to flat surfaces of the legs and clamp.

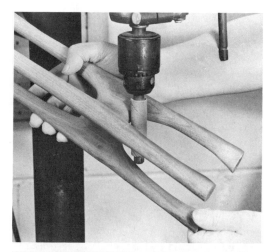

WITH LEGS ASSEMBLED, complete contour sanding between legs. Use sanding drum chucked in drill press.

DRILL ¼-IN.-DIA. HOLE, ¼-in. up from bottom of base, from edge to center hole for lamp cord.

PILOT HOLES for screws are drilled up through base into legs; assembly is test-fitted before gluing.

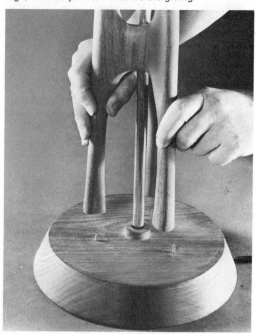

Spoonholder lamp

■ A COLLECTION of old or decorative spoons is of little more than sentimental value unless it is attractively displayed. A novel way to keep spoons in view is to suspend them from a spoon-holding lamp on a dining-room table, buffet, or in some other appropriate location. Making such a display is easy and consists mainly of fashioning a slotted disc which is then installed on an existing table lamp.

Lamp design and construction will, of course, pretty much determine the precise position of the disc on the column as well as the size of the center (mounting) hole. When planning the project, bear in mind that usually it is desirable to use a lamp that lets you place the disc at least 3 in. below the bottom of the lamp socket. (Some lamp designs will allow the disc nearer to the socket.)

The lamp shown had a column consisting of a number of metal tubes, washers and glass knobs strung on a length of iron pipe. Thus it was easy to insert the disc below the top tube and above the decorative glass knob.

The disc here is a 6-in. plastic saucer, colored to match the glass knobs, which you can buy almost anywhere. Before buying one, select your lamp and determine what diameter would harmonize best with the lamp's design.

You can make the spoonholding disc from almost any material having a thickness up to ¼ in. if it has a color or can take a paint finish. (Plywood, Plexiglas, Bakelite and the like are all good choices.) You could also use a metal, such as brass, but it might tend to mar the spoons unless the notches are carefully finished and padded with a glued-on felt.

When you cut the notches, size them so the spoons will fit snugly. Since spoon designs may vary, it's wise to cut a test template of cardboard or scrap plywood. Each spoon can then be custom-fitted to its matching notch.

The spoons shown are suspended bowls up. The drawing shows how the notches were cut in the rather tough plastic saucer. Two holes were drilled side by side, ⅜ in. from the rim, and two slots were made from each hole to the rim using a hacksaw. The in-between waste was then broken out. To finish, file each notch smooth to contour.

The center hole was made by drilling a pilot hole and using a tapered reamer to enlarge it to fit over the pipe that forms the lamp-column core.

SPOON HANDLE NOTCHES are roughed out with drill and saw. A file is used to shape and smooth the cuts.

HOLDER is sandwiched between glass knob and tubing. Socket is then tightened to hold it firmly.

COMPLETED DISC is slipped over pipe. Make certain to allow enough clearance for spoon bowls.

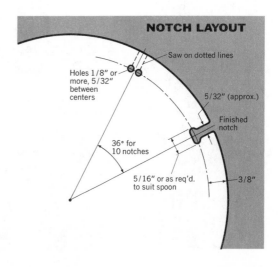

NOTCH LAYOUT

Saw on dotted lines

Holes 1/8" or more, 5/32" between centers

5/32" (approx.)

Finished notch

36° for 10 notches

5/16" or as req'd. to suit spoon

3/8"

Game area lighting

■ ONCE YOU DECIDE to set aside a portion of your property for lawn games, it makes good sense to extend their use into the evening by providing adequate illumination. In fact, during the blistering hot months, you'll probably find the youngsters using the games more during the cool after-dinner hours.

There are other factors to bear in mind when laying out your lighting. There may be times

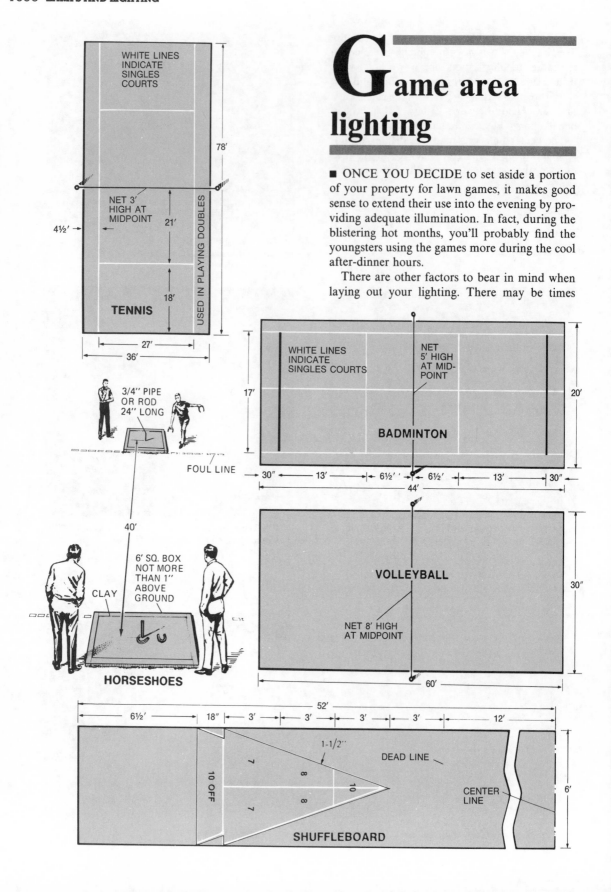

WHITE LINES INDICATE SINGLES COURTS

78′

NET 3′ HIGH AT MIDPOINT

4½′

21′

18′

USED IN PLAYING DOUBLES

TENNIS

27′

36′

3/4″ PIPE OR ROD 24″ LONG

FOUL LINE

40′

CLAY

6′ SQ. BOX NOT MORE THAN 1″ ABOVE GROUND

HORSESHOES

WHITE LINES INDICATE SINGLES COURTS

NET 5′ HIGH AT MID-POINT

17′

20′

BADMINTON

30″   13′   6½′   6½′   13′   30″

44′

VOLLEYBALL

NET 8′ HIGH AT MIDPOINT

30″

60′

52′

6½′   18″   3′   3′   3′   3′   12′

10 OFF

7   8   10

7   8

1-1/2″

DEAD LINE

CENTER LINE

6′

SHUFFLEBOARD

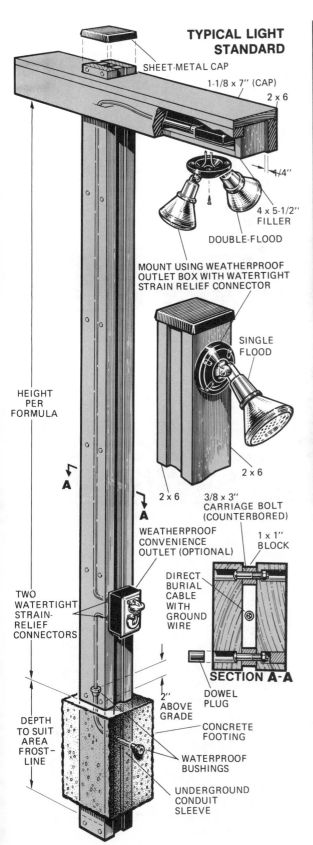

TYPICAL LIGHT STANDARD

SHEET-METAL CAP

1-1/8 x 7'' (CAP)

2 x 6

1/4''

4 x 5-1/2'' FILLER

DOUBLE-FLOOD

MOUNT USING WEATHERPROOF OUTLET BOX WITH WATERTIGHT STRAIN RELIEF CONNECTOR

SINGLE FLOOD

2 x 6

2 x 6

3/8 x 3'' CARRIAGE BOLT (COUNTERBORED)

1 x 1'' BLOCK

HEIGHT PER FORMULA

A

A

WEATHERPROOF CONVENIENCE OUTLET (OPTIONAL)

DIRECT BURIAL CABLE WITH GROUND WIRE

TWO WATERTIGHT STRAIN-RELIEF CONNECTORS

SECTION A-A

DOWEL PLUG

2'' ABOVE GRADE

CONCRETE FOOTING

WATERPROOF BUSHINGS

UNDERGROUND CONDUIT SLEEVE

DEPTH TO SUIT AREA FROST-LINE

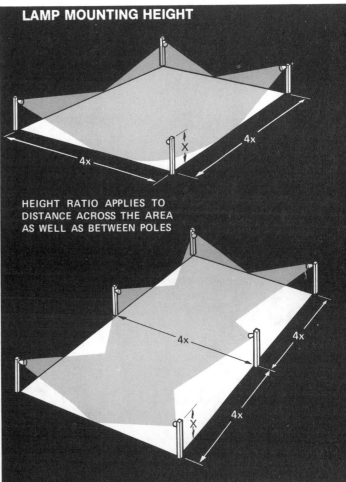

LAMP MOUNTING HEIGHT

4x

X

4x

HEIGHT RATIO APPLIES TO DISTANCE ACROSS THE AREA AS WELL AS BETWEEN POLES

4x

4x

X

4x

TYPICAL YARD-LIGHT STANCHION shown at left, can be varied to suit house architecture. The four-times mounting ratio shown above applies to the width of area as well as the distance between the poles. For example, if the court width is 40 ft., the pole height should be 10 ft. and the poles should be spaced no more than 40 ft. apart whether mercury or filament bulbs are used for light.

when you do not wish to light a game but want to make aesthetic use of the light for highlighting rock gardens, fish pools and the like. For barbecues, picnics and social gatherings you will want a lower level of illumination. Thus, when possible, utilize dimmer switches in your controls. And, in the typical light standard if at all possible, provide watertight convenience outlets. At some later date, you might decide to relocate a patio or purchase an electric mower.

• First, the game's location—which of course will determine the placement of lighting standards—should be considered carefully to avoid annoying neighbors.

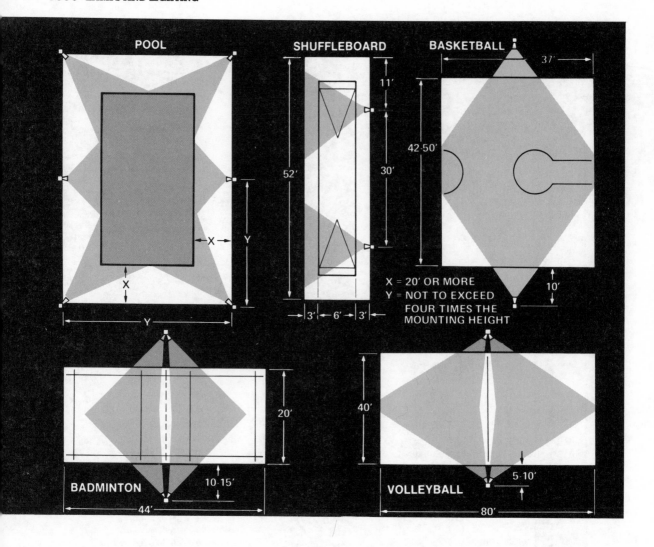

POOL

SHUFFLEBOARD

BASKETBALL

X = 20' OR MORE
Y = NOT TO EXCEED
FOUR TIMES THE
MOUNTING HEIGHT

BADMINTON

VOLLEYBALL

- A major consideration in the design of any direct-lighting system is the uniformity of illumination over the entire playing surface. A "hot spot" can be as distracting to a player as staring into the sun.

- Since filament lamps tend to have a short lamp life, mercury luminaires, designed for 24,000 burning hours per year, are recommended by most experts.

Though good illumination for a particular game is of primary concern, do give some thought to how the lights (and their poles) will look during the day.

Above are shown the most common back-yard games and the lighting setup best suited for each. Normally, 10 footcandles of illumination are recommended for all activities shown except shuffleboard. For this game, five footcandles are sufficient. Tennis courts (not illustrated above) require 10 footcandles of illumination. Swim-ming-pool lighting refers to pole lights placed around the pool.

Another advantage of well-planned activity and general outdoor lighting, is that such illumination can be utilized for security. So, you might also consider installing timers or light-sensitive switches that will turn lights on and off at predetermined times.

Outdoor floodlighting can be installed with either overhead or underground wiring, but from the standpoint of appearance, and for minimal interference, the latter is more desirable. An underground system can use either direct-burial cable conductors or wire in conduit. While overhead lines can be less costly, they may require additional items. For example, extra poles may be needed to keep wires from dangling into a playing area, or guys may be required on poles where there is a change in direction of feeders or where the feeders dead-end.

Night lighting transforms your yard

■ NOT TOO LONG AGO, outdoor residential lighting consisted of little more than placing a few floodlights around the grounds in rather bare-looking fixtures. Usually, these functional lights were affixed to buildings or parked on poles to provide broad, general illumination for safety and security for family and visitors.

Though safety and security are both still good and valid reasons for lighting your property at night, a third consideration—beautification—now plays an equally important role in outdoor lighting. Actually, ''lightscaping'' is simply an outside extension of indoor lighting. But if it's carefully done, you can add new dimensions to your home environment to create, in effect, a totally new living area.

Don't think that lighting your property automatically means that you will be using energy capriciously. For one thing, when exterior lights are turned on for outdoor family use, it means that indoor lights can be turned off or used minimally.

Additionally, you can save even more by installing a low-voltage outdoor system. How such systems work is explained on the next page.

This article shows you how to create attractive outdoor lighting effects—for greater safety and enjoyment—through the variety of fixtures and lamps now available. With these, plus a generous helping of your own imagination, you will be able to turn your backyard into a nighttime wonderland.

Basics of outdoor lighting

There is no great mystery to successful outdoor lighting, but there are basic principles you should know about. For example, be aware that it is important to avoid flat lighting—a look that is inevitable if you try to duplicate daylight. Instead, plan light placement so you create a scene with highlights and shadows that has a painting or sketchlike quality.

Generally, a touch of light here and there, cast by the appropriate fixture, is the kind of lighting

THIS ROOFTOP view shows the position of three 300-watt PAR units aimed at the lawn and trees for dramatic effect.

A BAMBOO trellis is cross-lighted by two floodlamps. A 75-watt lamp adds interesting shadow shapes.

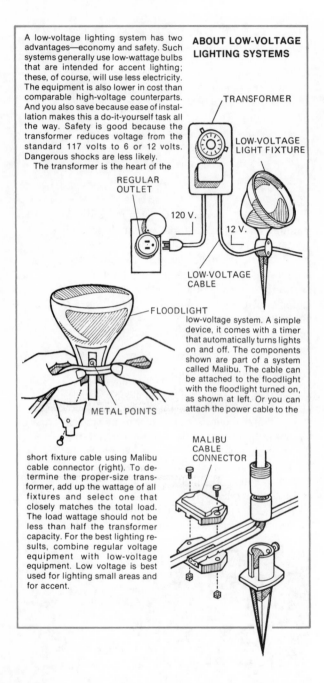

ABOUT LOW-VOLTAGE LIGHTING SYSTEMS

A low-voltage lighting system has two advantages—economy and safety. Such systems generally use low-wattage bulbs that are intended for accent lighting; these, of course, will use less electricity. The equipment is also lower in cost than comparable high-voltage counterparts. And you also save because ease of installation makes this a do-it-yourself task all the way. Safety is good because the transformer reduces voltage from the standard 117 volts to 6 or 12 volts. Dangerous shocks are less likely.

The transformer is the heart of the

TRANSFORMER

LOW-VOLTAGE
LIGHT FIXTURE

REGULAR
OUTLET

120 V.

12 V.

LOW-VOLTAGE
CABLE

FLOODLIGHT

low-voltage system. A simple device, it comes with a timer that automatically turns lights on and off. The components shown are part of a system called Malibu. The cable can be attached to the floodlight with the floodlight turned on, as shown at left. Or you can attach the power cable to the

METAL POINTS

MALIBU
CABLE
CONNECTOR

short fixture cable using Malibu cable connector (right). To determine the proper-size transformer, add up the wattage of all fixtures and select one that closely matches the total load. The load wattage should not be less than half the transformer capacity. For the best lighting results, combine regular voltage equipment with low-voltage equipment. Low voltage is best used for lighting small areas and for accent.

that will give your nighttime setting a charm of its own. And that's what you should aim for—a look that is distinctly different from your yard's daytime appearance.

Shielding fixtures are frequently used today even though they're slightly less efficient and, thus, more expensive to operate. On the plus side, however, these do eliminate irritating glare yet provide illumination where it is wanted. Local or border lighting and spotlighting are usually based more upon esthetics than the ability to see.

One way to determine how and where to place various light fixtures is by working with long extension cords and incandescent lamps. By using this trick you can fiddle with a number of lighting arrangements until you find a setup you'd like to make permanent.

Play it safe. All electric fixtures and wiring used for outside lighting must be weatherproof and installed in accordance with the National Electric Code (as well as your local building department).

About outdoor lamps

Currently, many installations use a floodlight holder for incandescent lamps with built-in reflectors (PAR). Some holders shield the entire lamp so that indoor lamps can be used. Others shield only the lamp base; with these you must use outdoor (weatherproof) lamps.

Outdoor incandescents are available in colors if you want to emphasize color, control insect attraction or create special-effect foliage lighting.

Tungsten halogen lamps are generally tubular in shape. These longer-life incandescents are generally used in higher-wattage floodlights.

You can use fluorescents outdoors provided you meet three criteria:
• Use only weatherproof fixtures.
• Make certain ballasts and fixtures are designed for use at below-freezing temperatures.
• Lamps exposed to temperatures ranging from 32° to 50° F. must be enclosed.

High-intensity discharge lamps (HID) are used for floodlighting larger areas and are not commonly used in residential outdoor lighting.

There is a wide variety of lamps and fixtures available to suit all outdoor lighting needs; typical shapes are shown on these pages.

Ideas for lightscaping

• *Automation*. Consider installing equipment which will turn lights on and off automatically. It

LOW-VOLTAGE UNITS under an overhang light planters and a rock garden. The transformer is in the soffit.

Many lamps and fixtures are available. The typical units shown here are usually made of brass, steel, copper or aluminum. The bulbs shown at right are the most commonly used 115-120-volt types. The reflector bulbs must be used in fixtures, while the PAR type (not shown) need no shielding because they are made of hard glass that will not crack due to weather

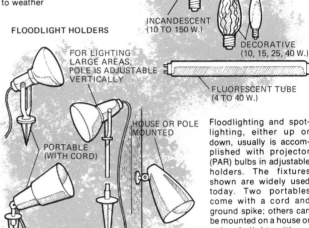

REFLECTOR BULB
(30, 50, 75, 150, 300 W.)

PROJECTOR BULB (75, 100 W. ; 100 W. IN 7 COLORS

INCANDESCENT (10 TO 150 W.)

DECORATIVE (10, 15, 25, 40 W.)

FLUORESCENT TUBE (4 TO 40 W.)

FLOODLIGHT HOLDERS

FOR LIGHTING LARGE AREAS, POLE IS ADJUSTABLE VERTICALLY

HOUSE OR POLE MOUNTED

PORTABLE (WITH CORD)

BALLAST TYPE (FOR 100 W. VAPOR PAR BULB)

Floodlighting and spotlighting, either up or down, usually is accomplished with projector (PAR) bulbs in adjustable holders. The fixtures shown are widely used today. Two portables come with a cord and ground spike; others can be mounted on a house or pole. A light with an adjustable-height pole is ideal for large-area illumination

The Bug Chaser bulb above has a special yellow coating. Border lights (left) seem to sparkle because of perforated housings. These come in varied heights

To light steps, paths and borders, select fixtures having neither glass nor plastic parts because the resulting glare will be annoying. Fixtures for this use range from 6 to 18 in. in diameter and 8 to 30 in. tall. From a wide selection you can pick fixtures that give downlighting for steps, borders or low plantings. Designs vary considerably; simply choose fixtures compatible with your garden and lighting needs

BORDER AND STEP FIXTURES

AREA DOWN LIGHTS

LOUVER LIGHT

TYPICAL BORDER LIGHTS

RECESSED STEP LIGHT

is relatively inexpensive and can save many dollars over the course of a season by completely eliminating wasted electricity.

• *Accent lighting.* Trees, shrubbery and the like can be mood-lighted by directing accent lights from above or below. Use such lights in addition to soft tinted, directed or reflected lighting. Keep in mind that overall floodlighting tends to "whitewash" a garden; accent lights are your best tools for avoiding that much-dreaded look.

• *Eliminate hazards.* Walks, steps and paths should be lighted to avoid any chance of missteps, falls and injuries. Do not use any bright or glaring fixtures on steps because they are too

UP-LIGHT FIXTURES

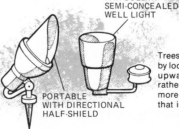

PAR BULB IN SEMI-CONCEALED WELL LIGHT

PORTABLE WITH DIRECTIONAL HALF-SHIELD

Trees, shrubbery and fences are lighted by locating fixtures on the ground, aimed upward. To produce a dimensional rather than flat appearance, direct two or more up-lights at an angle to the feature that is being specially lighted

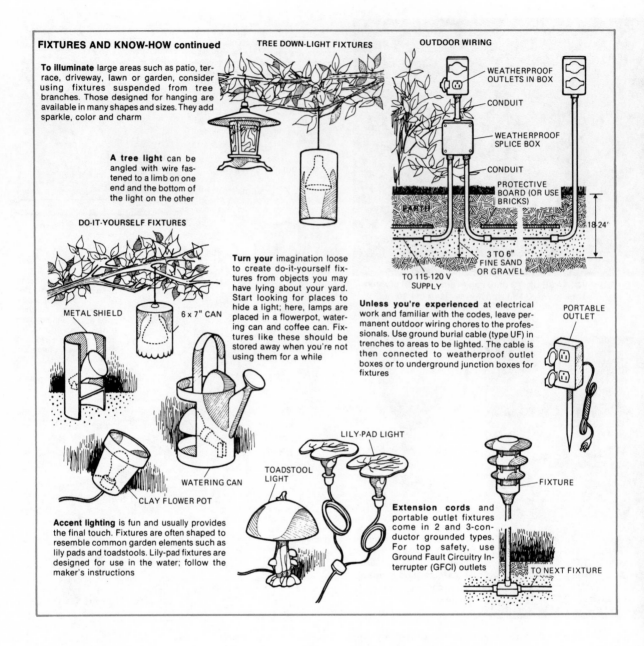

FIXTURES AND KNOW-HOW continued

TREE DOWN-LIGHT FIXTURES

OUTDOOR WIRING

To illuminate large areas such as patio, terrace, driveway, lawn or garden, consider using fixtures suspended from tree branches. Those designed for hanging are available in many shapes and sizes. They add sparkle, color and charm

A tree light can be angled with wire fastened to a limb on one end and the bottom of the light on the other

WEATHERPROOF OUTLETS IN BOX

CONDUIT

WEATHERPROOF SPLICE BOX

CONDUIT

PROTECTIVE BOARD (OR USE BRICKS)

EARTH

18-24'

3 TO 6" FINE SAND OR GRAVEL

TO 115-120 V SUPPLY

DO-IT-YOURSELF FIXTURES

Turn your imagination loose to create do-it-yourself fixtures from objects you may have lying about your yard. Start looking for places to hide a light; here, lamps are placed in a flowerpot, watering can and coffee can. Fixtures like these should be stored away when you're not using them for a while

Unless you're experienced at electrical work and familiar with the codes, leave permanent outdoor wiring chores to the professionals. Use ground burial cable (type UF) in trenches to areas to be lighted. The cable is then connected to weatherproof outlet boxes or to underground junction boxes for fixtures

PORTABLE OUTLET

METAL SHIELD

6 x 7" CAN

WATERING CAN

CLAY FLOWER POT

Accent lighting is fun and usually provides the final touch. Fixtures are often shaped to resemble common garden elements such as lily pads and toadstools. Lily-pad fixtures are designed for use in the water; follow the maker's instructions

TOADSTOOL LIGHT

LILY-PAD LIGHT

Extension cords and portable outlet fixtures come in 2 and 3-conductor grounded types. For top safety, use Ground Fault Circuitry Interrupter (GFCI) outlets

FIXTURE

TO NEXT FIXTURE

likely to blind step users. Ideally, fixtures for step lighting conceal all bulbs yet provide desired safety lighting. Often the locating of fixtures behind foliage will hide lamps, too.

• *Dining out.* For patios and the like, you want lighting that will draw everyone together into a group. Try for good visibility without harsh, irritating light.

Keep in mind that you should also have some transitional lighting on the fringe area so that the change from lighted to dark areas will not be too sudden.

• *Lawn games.* Most games can be adequately illuminated using two poles 18 to 20 ft. high with two or more 150-watt flood bulbs per pole. For net games, light poles should be about 3 ft. from each end of the net. Regardless of the game, place fixtures so light will not shine in players' eyes.

A final word. When you plan your outdoor lighting arrangement, don't overlook your neighbors' right to privacy. Aim all of the lights toward your own property—not theirs—or you will almost certainly trigger squabbles every time you turn on your lights.

Landscaping that's down to earth

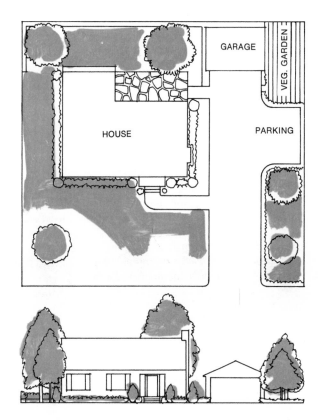

■ IF YOU WANT to do an effective job of landscaping—or relandscaping—your home, start by spending a little time analyzing how you use the ground you have. Then design the plantings, gardens, walks and other elements to give you and your family the greatest benefits. The finished product should enhance your life style.

Professionals recognize that there are five general types of use around the average home. Consider these as you think about your own family activities:

Public area. The front yard, the walk to the door, the view of the house from the street.

Living area. That part of the yard you use for outdoor living, barbecues and entertaining. It can include a patio and a screened porch. It is usually at the back of the house.

Play area. The need for a play area varies widely from family to family. The lawn may include a childrens' area with playground equipment, a space for adult games such as badminton, or a swimming pool.

Garden area. Should there be room for a vegetable garden, or a flower garden? Flowers, of course, may be used in beds throughout your plan, but if someone in the family has gardening as a hobby, a special area should be set aside.

Service area. Every home needs an area for certain services: a place to hang clothes, to store the garbage cans, or perhaps to store gardening and maintenance equipment.

After thinking about your family's needs and the different types of yard areas, the next step is to produce a plan on paper. You can buy graph paper at your stationery store. It will help you draw your plan in scale. The easiest scale to follow is ¼ in. on paper equaling 1 ft. in your yard.

Begin by sketching in the permanent structures—your home, concrete walks which are already laid, the driveway. Then draw in all big trees. Locate the trunk by using a small circle on the paper, then use a dotted line to indicate the spread of the branches.

The easiest and least expensive way to relandscape is to work your way around existing trees and walks. However, if they present really serious problems, you can consider removing them. There is no point in living with the mistakes made by earlier owners.

Eventually you must arrive at a final plan. The real value of the final plan is that it enables you to plan your work over a long period of time. Once you know exactly what you want to do, you can break the job into parts and spread it over months or even years.

The elements to use. A good landscaping plan is a combination of elements joined together to provide both beauty and practical use.

Open lawn: Large open lawns give a sense of spaciousness, but must be planned for areas which receive sufficient sun.

Walks: You can use concrete, brick, flagstone, railroad ties—any material which provides needed footing. Select your material for appearance and for ease of care. Concrete is easy to shovel clear of snow in the winter, flagstone is not. Brick walks are easier to relocate than concrete.

Fences: Use fences for privacy, for yard division, and for optical effect. Fences, because they enclose, tend to make the yard feel smaller, cozier. An unlimited number of fence designs gives you all the choice you need.

Raised beds: Raised beds, built up with brick, stone or wood, are a good way to break up a flat, uninteresting space.

Structures: Small outstructures, such as gazebos or sheds for maintenance equipment, if well designed, can enhance your yard.

Patios: Poured concrete, brick, stone, wood—nearly every material can be used to lay out patio living space. Begin your design of the living area by laying out a patio, then working out from it.

Steps: If your lot is hilly, steps can be an eye-pleasing addition.

Pools: Tiny concrete pools for flowers and fish offer an interesting method of enhancing your yard.

Bushes and shrubs: Consider these as tools in your landscaping. Use them as foundation plantings, as feature plantings, or as screens.

Trees: Trees are a valuable asset to any home, and increase the sale value. You use them for shade, to frame and decorate the house, and as a screen. Flowering and ornamental trees have an additional decorative value, while fruit trees in many cases add even more value.

Select trees carefully and place them on your lot with even greater care. You must remember that the 6 or 8-ft. sapling you buy now will be a full-grown tree some day—and you must allow enough room for that inevitable growth.

WHEN YOU PLANT A TREE, you must consider the long-range effect. Refer to the chart below to get an idea of the eventual height, spread, and overall shape of the tree you select. This chart shows the average measurements of a mature tree—and the age of maturity differs from species to species. However, most trees will occupy near-full space in from 10 to 20 years.

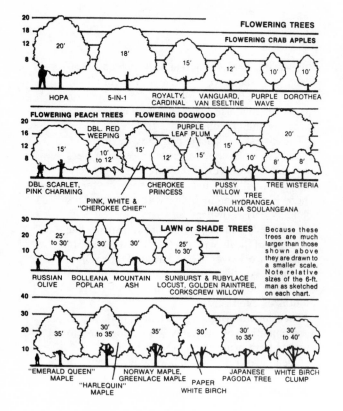

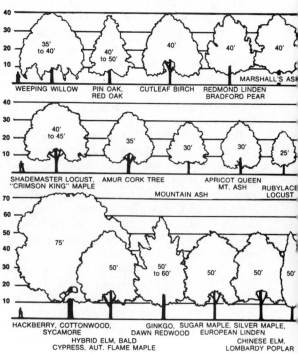

Don't plant young trees too close to your house. They must be far enough away so that when full grown they don't brush against the walls and make painting and other maintenance difficult. If you plan a garden area, remember that it should have full sun for most of each day. If you plant a tree nearby, think ahead to the day when it casts a shadow. You may end up with no garden at all if the tree eventually blocks out the sun.

If your plan includes large lawn areas, keep in mind that growing trees will eventually shade the grass, too. Grass is difficult to grow in dense shade, and you may have to change the shaded parts of the lawn—putting in a ground cover in place of the grass.

One of the reasons you plant a tree is, of course, for the cooling shade it provides. One of the important advantages of a landscaping plan is that through it you can recognize eventual changes which must be made—such as replacing grass with ground cover when the time comes.

Talk with your nurseryman about the trees which grow best in your area. He can advise you about disease-resistant trees, growth rates and maintenance requirements, such as annual spraying. Shade trees are undergoing major changes today, brought about by improved propagation techniques and widespread research activities.

The thrust of the research has been to develop trees that grow faster, are disease-resistant, and pollution-tolerant.

In planting trees at the front of your house, try to frame the building. Plant the trees at the sides and slightly to the front. Tall trees in the back yard eventually serve as a pretty background when the house is viewed from the street. Large trees, planted directly in front of the house, can be useful in screening the noise of heavy traffic, and in providing privacy if you live on a busy thoroughfare. But if yours is a quiet residential street, it usually is better to keep the front of the house open.

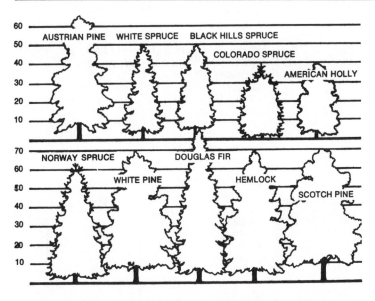

EVERGREEN TREES provide shade all year and are outstanding as a winter windbreaker. Evergreens generally have a smaller spread than deciduous varieties, and so can be planted closer to the house. In time, some evergreens, such as the Douglas fir, will reach great heights—100 feet and more—but they are relatively slow growing. For use near the house, however, it usually is better to plant shorter types.

Shrubbery for your landscaping

■ WHEN PLANNING the landscaping for your home, look to shrubs to provide accents, color, low sweeping lines, and year-round interest.

The term "shrubs" takes in a wide variety of growing things and before you complete the final landscape plan for your home, you should become familiar with some of the shrubs available. Tour well-planted neighborhoods and learn to identify the shrubs you see. Visit a nursery and see what kinds of shrubs are available in your area.

You might begin by dividing shrubs into three categories: the flowering deciduous; the broadleaf evergreens; and the needle evergreens.

The flowering shrubs include such colorful beauties as the dogwood, forsythia, honeysuckle, mockorange and spiraea. Most bloom in the spring and there are varieties which thrive in nearly every climate.

Broadleaf evergreens generally favor the southern sections of the country, though varieties have been developed which grow as far north as southern Wisconsin. To learn what types are available to you, visit your friendly nursery. The broadleafs include azaleas, euonymus, holly, mountain laurel, and the rhododendron, among others.

Needle evergreens include the whole family of junipers, the yews and arborvitae. Most of these can be grown all the way to the Canadian border.

Look at the chart on the next page for a list of shrubs of all three types. In the chart, you'll find the average height each species is likely to reach and the type of light which it prefers. But if your favorite shrub isn't listed, don't despair. Check with your nursery first, because many new and hardier types are developed each year.

Shrubs can be used in dozens of interesting ways around your lot. You can group them into

HEDGE	CLIPPED OR INFORMAL	HEIGHT (in ft.)	EVERGREEN OR DECIDUOUS
Barberry, Japanese	Unclipped	1½–3	D
Korean boxwood	Clipped	2	E
True dwarf boxwood	Either	3	E
Russian olive	Either	15	D
Bigleaf wintercreeper	Either	4	E
Japanese holly	Either	3	E
Canaert juniper	Clipped	5	E
Amur River privet	Clipped	1½–4	D
Regel's privet	Clipped	3	D
Dwarf honeysuckle	Unclipped	4	D
Tatarian honeysuckle	Unclipped	8	D
Pachistima canbyi	Either	1	E
Dwarf ninebark	Clipped	2	D
Colorado spruce	Either	5	E
Alpine currant	Either	3	D
Bridal wreath spiraea	Unclipped	5	D
Persian lilac	Unclipped	8	D
Hicks yew	Either	4	E
American arborvitae	Clipped	5	E
Hemlock	Clipped	8	E
Viburnum opulus nanum	Unclipped	2	D

THE HEDGES SHOWN in this chart are shrubs which are particularly suited for planting in long rows for fencing, to screen an unwanted view, or as a baffle to cut down undesirable noise. Flowering shrubs such as forsythia, lilac or weigela should never be clipped to formal shapes.

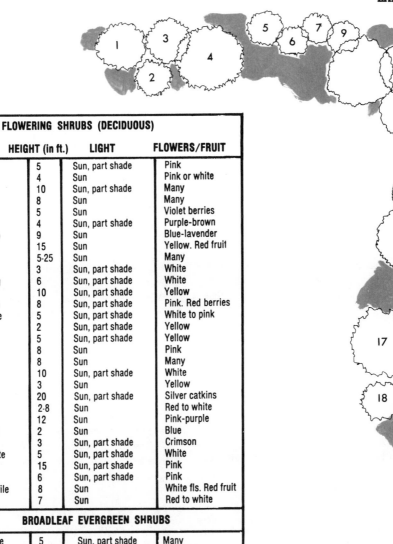

FLOWERING SHRUBS (DECIDUOUS)

NAME	HEIGHT (in ft.)	LIGHT	FLOWERS/FRUIT
Abelia	5	Sun, part shade	Pink
Almond, flowering	4	Sun	Pink or white
Althaea	10	Sun, part shade	Many
Buddleia	8	Sun	Many
Callicarpa	5	Sun	Violet berries
Calycanthus	4	Sun, part shade	Purple-brown
Chaste tree (vitex)	9	Sun	Blue-lavender
Cherry, Cornelian	15	Sun	Yellow. Red fruit
Crape-myrtle	5-25	Sun	Many
Deutzia	3	Sun, part shade	White
Dogwood, red-twig	6	Sun, part shade	White
Forsythia	10	Sun, part shade	Yellow
Honeysuckle, bush	8	Sun, part shade	Pink. Red berries
Hydrangea, Peegee	5	Sun, part shade	White to pink
Hypericum	2	Sun, part shade	Yellow
Kerria	5	Sun, part shade	Yellow
Kolkwitzia	8	Sun	Pink
Lilac, French	8	Sun	Many
Mockorange	10	Sun, part shade	White
Potentilla	3	Sun	Yellow
Pussy willow	20	Sun, part shade	Silver catkins
Quince, flowering	2-8	Sun	Red to white
Smoke tree	12	Sun	Pink-purple
Spiraea, Blue Mist	2	Sun	Blue
Spiraea, red	3	Sun, part shade	Crimson
Spiraea, Van Houtte	5	Sun, part shade	White
Tamarix	15	Sun, part shade	Pink
Viburnum carlesi	6	Sun, part shade	Pink
Viburnum, doublefile	8	Sun	White fls. Red fruit
Weigela	7	Sun	Red to white

BROADLEAF EVERGREEN SHRUBS

NAME	HEIGHT (in ft.)	LIGHT	FLOWERS/FRUIT
Azalea, Glenn Dale	5	Sun, part shade	Many
Azalea, Flame	6	Part shade	Warm colors
Barberry, wintergreen	5	Sun	Black berries
Boxwood, English	20	Sun, part shade	
Boxwood, littleleaf	3	Sun, part shade	
Cotoneaster, bearberry	1	Sun, part shade	Red berries
Daphne, rose	1	Sun, part shade	Pink. Fragrant
Euonymus japonica	10	Sun	Pink berries
Euonymus, spreading	6	Sun/shade	Pink-red berries
Holly, Burford	6	Sun, part shade	Red berries
Holly, Japanese	5-10	Sun, part shade	Black berries
Holly, Oregon grape	4	Sun, part shade	Yellow Blue berries
Laurel, Mountain	6	Sun, part shade	Pink to white
Leucothoe	3	Shade	White
Osmanthus ilicifolius	8	Sun, part shade	White
Pieris japonica	10	Part shade	White
Pyracantha	8	Sun	Orange berries
Rhododendron	8	Part shade	Many colors

NEEDLE EVERGREEN SHRUBS

NAME	HEIGHT (in ft.)	LIGHT	FLOWERS/FRUIT
Arborvitae, globe	3	Sun/shade	
Juniper, Andorra	1½	Sun, part shade	
Juniper, Keteleer	12	Sun, part shade	
Juniper, Pfitzer	4	Sun, light shade	
Pine, Mugho	5	Sun	
Yew, Hicks	6	Sun/shade	
Yew, Japanese spreading	5	Shade	

SHRUBS CAN PROVIDE flowers or berries almost year-round. The typical border plan shown here needs a sunny place about 10×60 feet, and will provide spring-to-frost flowers and berries. Shrubs are 1. doublefile viburnum; 2. abelia; 3. pyracantha; 4. Andorra juniper; 5. lilac; 6. callicarpa; 7. tamarix; 8. buddleia; 9. forsythia; 10. crape-myrtle; 11. smoke tree; 12. Blue Mist spiraea; 13. potentilla; 14. mockorange; 15. hypericum; 16. pussy willow; 17. Japanese holly; 18. red spiraea; 19. red-twig dogwood; and 20. deutzia.

small green islands to break up large lawn areas. You can arrange them as hedges, in long rows, with the eventual height being determined by the species you select.

If you have put in trees at either end of the house, the sweeping line of the shrubs at the base of the house will seem to tie the whole picture together.

A row of tall shrubs at the back of your lot is often a better way than a fence to divide your lot from your neighbors. If you don't want the curtain between the two properties to be too much of a wall, keep the shrubs trimmed to four feet.

Use shrubs as hedges

The idea of using shrubs for hedges can be important, depending on the landscaping problems you have to solve. You can grow hedges ranging from as little as one foot in height up to 15 or more feet. You can allow a hedge to grow in its natural shape, or you can clip it to the shape you desire.

The list of hedge plants includes the majority of the most popular shrubs used for hedges. Some are deciduous, some are evergreen. Some will flower, some will be festooned with colorful berries.

The very smallest hedges provide an interesting and natural way to divide your yard without really breaking it up. You can set apart a patch for a garden by surrounding the area with a tiny privet. It shouldn't be high enough to break up the view across your yard or to shade the sun from the garden, yet it should have the effect of setting the area neatly apart.

Tall shrubs planted behind a flower garden provide a green backdrop which shows off your flower blooms to great advantage. If you have flowering shrubs, you will be rewarded with a burst of color in the background planting early in the spring, followed later by the color of the garden itself. When planning this use, place the shrubs so they don't shade the garden too much. A flower garden on the south side of a planting of shrubs is best.

In planning the use of shrubs, particularly at the front of your house, think in terms of what the eye sees—lines, and color and mass. You have the vertical lines provided by the trees, the vertical and horizontal lines of the house itself, and the low horizontal lines provided by shrubs to work with. For mass, when you need it, you can group shrubs of different heights. For color you have not only the green of the lawn and the color of the exterior of the house, but you have a variety of greens, blue-greens and yellow-greens among the shrubs—not to mention reds and grays.

Your objective is to blend these lines, colors and masses into a harmonious whole. Through plantings you tie the house to the ground and make it a part of the natural environment—instead of a foreign structure superimposed on it.

Ground covers

Ground cover plants, though not actually shrubbery, must also be included in your landscaping plan. They provide answers in problem areas, for example, where grass is difficult to mow or grow.

They also can be used ornamentally, in beds beside walks and at the base of the house, or even in small islands in the midst of the lawn. Ground covers provide an interesting variation in texture and color when you need it.

Good ground cover plants thrive in a wide range of soil and moisture conditions, and are relatively free from pests and disease. Three very hardy and popular ground covers are myrtle (Vinca major), pachysandra, and English ivy.

Other good evergreen ground covers worth investigating are ajuga, Cornus canadensis, lily-turf, sedum, heather, euonymus fortunei, and the creeping junipers. Look, too, at the dwarf spreading English and Canada yews.

Plant where mowing is difficult

Plant ground covers in areas where mowing would be difficult or inconvenient—the narrow area between the foundation of the house and the edge of the driveway, for example, or along a lot line between houses. If you have problems with growing things on the north side of the house, ground covers can solve this problem, too. Many of them do very well in areas where there is little or no sun.

Plant them around the base of a tree as a good substitute for the grass which refuses to grow there—or at the base of a fence, to make the fence more attractive and to eliminate the hand-trimming of grass which otherwise would grow there, too close to the fence for the mower to reach.

As with trees, when you plant shrubs keep in mind the size they will attain when mature. Give each shrub ample room to develop and to take on its attractive natural shape. Once a shrub has reached its mature size, it should be pruned or trimmed annually.

Wood lathe tips from an expert

■ THOUGH A WOOD LATHE is the one shop tool that almost guarantees shop satisfaction, many workshoppers shy away from the tool because they believe it takes some kind of "special" skill to master a lathe. If you have such reservations, you are depriving yourself of a great deal of shop fun and creative satisfaction.

For openers, the lathe is the *only* shop tool that will let you turn out a completed product all by itself. You can shape, glue, assemble and finish without ever leaving this remarkable tool.

It is not an exaggeration to say that you can, in fact, turn out a handsome project on your very first try by using scraping methods. But you do owe it to yourself to learn the basics before switching on the lathe.

About wood lathes

The label *wood lathe* is generally used when referring to a woodturning lathe to avoid any mixup or confusion with its cousin, the screw-cutting metalturning lathe.

A wood lathe is designated according to the maximum diameter of work which can be swung over its bed. Thus, a lathe that can handle a 12-in. diameter piece of wood is called a 12-in. lathe.

CONTRARY TO POPULAR misconception, it doesn't take a small fortune to get started in woodturning. Items in photos were turned on lathe above.

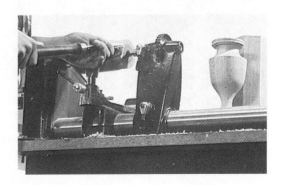

The important parts of a lathe can be seen in the photos. Basically, a lathe consists of a headstock, a tailstock and a toolrest. The latter is comprised of the rest itself mounted in a base that slides along the bed. There is a variety of rests available, and these can be interchanged to suit the task at hand. At the least you should have both 6- and 12-in. rests, as well as the right-angle rest for faceplate turning.

Though there are two types of headstock spindles, solid and hollow, most are hollow. The hollow spindle is internally tapered at both ends for a No. 2 Morse shank. Small lathes usually have a No. 1 Morse taper. Most manufacturers make the tailstock spindle to match the headstock so that the various attachments can be used at either end of the lathe if desired.

Adjustable tailstock

The tailstock is adjustable, of course, to suit the length of the work to be turned between cen-

ters; the headstock is fixed. The former can be moved along the bed and across the bed (slightly), and its spindle can be projected or retracted by turning the feed handle. Any and all tailstock spindle positions can be fixed by clamping.

Cutting tools

Basically, there are five shapes of chisels that you will have to learn about *and master*. The most important—and probably the first one that you will use—is the gouge. This is used for roughing cuts, making coves and other operations. The skew chisel is also important because it does the best job of smoothing cylinders and cutting beads, shoulders, V grooves and the like. It is also the most difficult chisel to master, which means that you should first practice with it using inexpensive scrap wood.

The spear (or diamond point) is used when its conformation matches the shape of the work. The

GUIDE TO THE LATHE CHISELS YOU'LL NEED

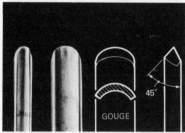

GOUGE IS THE cutting tool that you will use most often; its cutting edge is beveled on convex side (about 45°). Use a gouge for roughing out stock and to reduce stock to cylindrical shape. Gouges are available in widths from ¼ to 1 in.

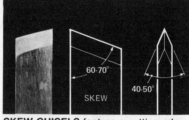

SKEW CHISELS feature a cutting edge that is at an angle to the side of the tool (around 70°). Generally both sides of the cutting edge are beveled as shown. Use skew to make V cuts, beads and tapers. Available in sizes from ⅛ to 1½ in.

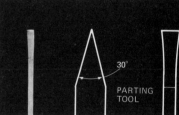

PARTING TOOL has flat sides and a square bottom, is used to make narrow grooves to desired depths. Note that the tool is thicker at the center of the blade than at the edges; center thickness determines cut width. Sizes from ½ to 1 in.

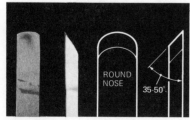

ROUND-NOSE chisel can be used for coves and the like in spindle turning, for concave cutting in faceplate turning (bowl interiors). The tool is used with a scraping action; a sharp one produces a very smooth cut. Sizes from ⅛ to 1 in.

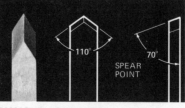

DIAMOND POINT chisel is also a scraping tool. It is used whenever its shape is needed to fit the turning being worked. The most common size used is ½ in. but you can grind other chisels to a diamond point to custom-suit the job at hand.

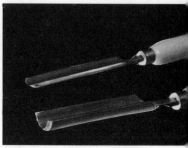

STANDARD GOUGE (top) and extra-deep gouge. The latter lets you rough-round stock incredibly fast.

HOW TO SHARPEN YOUR TURNING TOOLS

TO RESTORE cutting edge to correct angle, grind tool on wheel with true face.

GOUGE BEVEL can be ground as above or as in photo at left. Watch bevel carefully.

TO WHET gouge, pour oil on stone, stroke gouge using a circular motion.

AS GOUGE is moved in circular motion, rotate the edge from left to right.

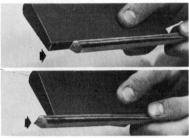

NEXT, SLIPSTONE is placed on concave side as at top, then pulled downward (bottom).

TO GRIND a skew, let bevel contact wheel face then move it back and forth.

NEXT, FLOP chisel and grind second side. Maintain correct angle.

TO WHET SKEW, pour oil on stone, keep bevel in contact, use figure-8 motion.

WHEN "WIRE" forms on edge, turn skew over and whet second bevel.

round-nose chisel is also used to suit work configuration. Both chisels are used with a scraping action.

The parting tool is a double-ground tool used for making sizing cuts and cutoffs.

You will also need a number of basic accessories. As your skills and knowledge develop, you will want to add other important accessories to your lathe setup.

Wood lathe safety

The lathe is a safe tool to use when you practice good shop safety habits. The usual power-tool rules apply—make certain tool is solidly affixed to a rigid base or cabinet, assure its being properly grounded to avoid chance of shock, and do wear clothes that are suitable for workshop activities: no dangling neckties, loose sleeves or long hairdos that could be caught in the spinning workpiece.

Several safety rules that apply especially to the lathe:

● Develop the technique of always spinning the work by hand before turning on power, to check clearance.

● Keep chisels sharp for easy cutting operations.

● Run all work at a safe, high (top) speed. More often than not, this means at speeds below 1000 rpm.

BASIC TURNING TECHNIQUES

1 SHAPING TO ROUGH round is done with a gouge; deep gouge used here works great and is fast.

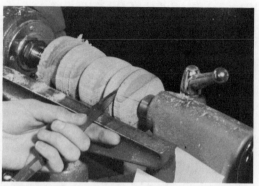

2 NEXT, USE the parting tool to cut to desired depths. Stop lathe and check cut often with a caliper.

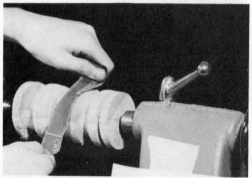

3 USE FINE, then very-fine sandpaper shoeshine fashion to smooth the turning spindle.

4 BEFORE REMOVING piece from the lathe, check its shape against a pattern for the turning.

5 FINAL SMOOTHING is done with 000 steel wool; note that the turning is now faceplate mounted.

OBJECTS FOR daily use are easy to turn.

6 FINISH IS APPLIED before stand is removed from lathe; next, it is glued into turned base.

HOLDING GOUGE in a shearing position gives clean, smooth cut, but scraping is better for beginners.

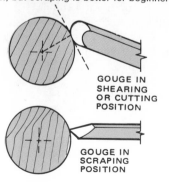

GOUGE IN
SHEARING
OR CUTTING
POSITION

GOUGE IN
SCRAPING
POSITION

TOOLS OF THE WOODTURNER'S TRADE

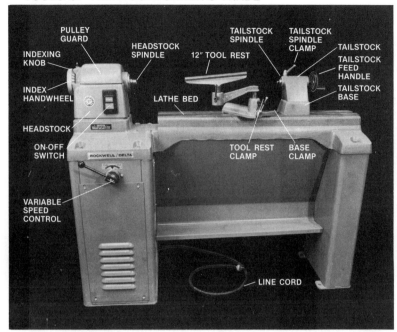

FAMILIARIZE YOURSELF with names and purposes of lathe components identified.

DRIVE CENTER fits into headstock spindle, turns the work between centers.

TOOLRESTS come in various sizes, shapes. Shown are 6- and 12-in., and right angle.

ASSORTMENT of inside and outside calipers is needed to check diameter of work.

CUP, OR DEAD, center is used at tailstock to support outboard end of spindle.

FACEPLATE is used for turning bowls; it is threaded onto the headstock spindle.

SCREW (LEFT), drive and spur centers; first is for small faceplate work.

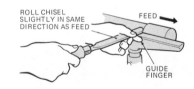

RIGHT WAY to rough a blank round; gouge is rolled slightly.

● Using a dust or respiratory mask is a personal choice. Some people don't when cutting, but you should *always wear one* when filing, sanding, dusting or finishing. You can get a low-cost mask with throwaway filter liner. Those with allergy problems should probably keep the mask on during all lathe operations.

● Lathe purists also argue that safety glasses are unnecessary because a tool torn from the operator's grip or a workpiece flung from the lathe tends to follow a downward path. Though the trajectory argument is valid, most prefer wearing safety goggles.

Turning on the faceplate

When the work cannot be turned between centers, it must be mounted on a faceplate or other workholding device. All cutting in faceplate work is done with chisels in the scraping manner.

If you should try to apply a shearing cut on the edge of a piece of faceplate-mounted work, you will probably produce a hogging cut. That is, the chisel will tear a chunk from the wood and, in turn, be torn from your hands because the end grain is presented twice to the operator on every revolution.

Once you have selected the stock for a faceplate turning, cut it square. Then cut the rough-round shape on a bandsaw, keeping the blade on the waste side of the line. Select the largest-diameter faceplate you can use on the workpiece. Mount the block as shown in the photos. Always

FACEPLATE TURNING BASICS

SQUARE UP STOCK, find center by marking diagonals using a straightedge.

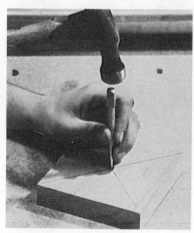

MAKE A permanent mark at the center by tapping a punch lightly.

WITH COMPASS, lay out and mark circle ⅛ in. larger than finished size.

USE BANDSAW to cut stock to rough dimension; cut on the waste side.

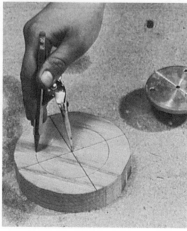

SELECT faceplate, set compass 1/16 in. more than its radius and draw a circle.

CENTER faceplate on stock, line up two screws with grain, mark for screwholes.

BORE PILOT holes for faceplate screws; use tape stop on bit at desired depth.

USE HEFTIEST possible screws to secure to faceplate; choose length carefully.

HOLDING LATHE spindle rigid, mount workpiece on lathe, tighten with wrench.

SET MACHINE at low speed, and scrape across edge of stock.

TO SHAPE the outside corner, a skew can be used in a scraping fashion.

AFTER SMOOTHING face with square-nose chisel, use pencil to mark cuts.

SMALL ROUND-NOSE chisel is used to turn decorative half-round groove.

BORE MORTISE for spindle stub with work still on lathe.

PULL SKEW BACK UNTIL CUTTING STARTS

FOR SMOOTHEST finish, you must master the skew.

use the heaviest possible screws to mount wood on a faceplate.

Generally, a woodturner shapes the outside diameter first with a square-nose chisel. Since there are no square-nose chisels available commercially, you'll have to grind your own. The best tool for final smoothing of an outside edge is the spear-point chisel. Use it to pick up a scant bite at one corner and carry the bite right across the edge.

Truing the work's face can be done with either a skew, square-nose or diamond-point chisel held in the scraping attitude. Move the tool from the center of the workpiece to its outside edge. You can shape the face with whatever chisel best fits the shape you want. Work from the center toward the edge. Remember, the outer edge is spinning much faster than the center. Thus, it is good practice to take light cuts only when working on the face.

Turning a spindle

Work turned between centers is called spindle turning. Make it your practice to square the wood you will use for a spindle turning; this makes it easier to rough-round a cylinder with a deep gouge. Steps for spindle turning are illustrated on these pages. It is important to determine the centers of both ends in order to mount the workpiece in the lathe properly. Other key points include:

● Always cut saw kerfs for the drive center. Use a wooden mallet to seat the drive center well into the wood. (A metal hammer will damage the center.)

● Apply a lubricant to the cup center to reduce friction. You can use light machine oil or a candle stub, which won't stain wood.

When mounting a piece to be spindle-turned, insert the spur center into the spindle and support the outboard end of the workpiece with your left hand. Move the tailstock within an inch of the work and clamp it. Advance the cup center by turning the handwheel; make certain its point enters the prepunched center. Continue to advance the center while slowly rotating the work with your left hand until the work is difficult to turn. Then back off the wheel ⅛ to ¼ turn and lock the tailstock spindle. Set the toolrest, rotate the work by hand to clear the rest and turn lathe on.

Make certain that screws are of the right length for the project; they mustn't come in contact with the chisels. (For some designs, conventional faceplate mounting cannot be used. Glue mounting, glue-chuck or ring-clamp methods are then required.) To turn the hurricane lamp base shown, you *can* use conventional faceplate mounting.

With the block securely fastened, turn the faceplate all the way onto the lathe spindle. If your lathe has a system for locking the spindle while you tighten the faceplate, use it. Adjust the toolrest so it is about ⅛ in. away from the work and the chisel's cutting edge will be at the center line. Rotate the work by hand to make certain it clears the toolrest. Run the machine at slow speed. Check the lathe manufacturer's speed chart because the roughing speed varies with the type and diameter of the wood.

Turn the work to a rough cylinder using the gouge and a slow speed. To smooth the cylinder, use the skew, a tool that requires effort and practice to master. Here's the easiest way for learning how: With the work spinning in the lathe, rest the skew on the toolrest so its point is well *over* the cylinder. Grip its handle with your right hand and the blade—close to toolrest—with your left hand. Curl your fingers over the blade so your thumb is toward you. (See photo.) Slowly lower the skew until its bevel rides on work and shearing cut is made at blade's center. Maintain blade position as you move skew across the cylinder.

Getting a professional finish

First, the wood should be thoroughly sanded, dusted and wiped with a tack rag. Next, prepare a clean, lint-free cloth with a small amount of shellac and boiled linseed oil. Then, upon application, set the lathe at slow to medium speed (about 600 rpm) and keep the rag moving to avoid burn marks in the shellac.

TURNING A SPINDLE

TO GLUE UP stock for spindle turning, apply liberal amount to surfaces.

USE A NUMBER of clamps to hold the work tight until glue dries.

IMMEDIATELY wipe off squeezed-out excess glue and set aside for 24 hours.

FIND CENTERS on both ends using diagonal lines method as shown here.

ON SPUR CENTER end of work, saw ⅛-in.-deep kerfs along diagonal lines.

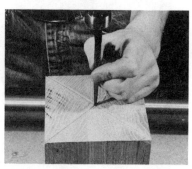

ON BOTH ENDS, center-punch holes at exact center (about 1/16 in. dia.)

USE A WOOD mallet, which won't damage center, to drive center into stock.

MOUNT WORK in lathe; before advancing cup center, apply lubricant.

ADVANCE cup center into stock until secure, back off ⅛th turn, lock.

IF WORK MUST be removed, mark at headstock using reference on spur.

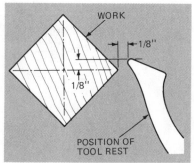

ADJUST toolrest as shown, clamp. Turn work by hand to make sure it clears.

USING GOUGE, rough-round right end, mark to determine cylinder size.

START LATHE and use gouge to make a series of 1½ to 2-in.-long cuts.

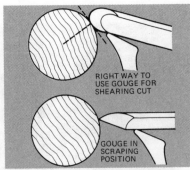

RIGHT WAY TO USE GOUGE FOR SHEARING CUT

GOUGE IN SCRAPING POSITION

GOUGE can be used to make a shearing or scraping cut; make light cuts.

WHEN YOU'RE about 2 in. from left end, roll gouge and work toward left.

USE SKEW with light shearing cut to turn cylinder smooth.

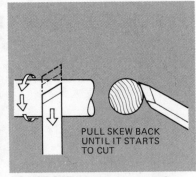

PULL SKEW BACK UNTIL IT STARTS TO CUT

TO USE SKEW, place it over work, draw it back until bevel rides work.

OR, MAKE smoothing cut using skew in scraping position.

USE A SQUARE to check cylinder flatness; remove stock as required.

CUT TEMPLATE and use it to lay out basic shape on cylinder.

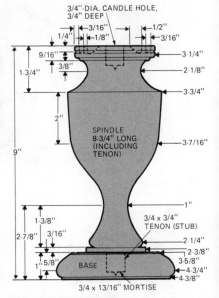

3/4''-DIA. CANDLE HOLE, 3/4'' DEEP

3/16''
1/4''
1/8''
1/2''
3/16''
9/16''
3/8''
1-3/4''
2''
9''
1-3/8''
2-7/8''
3/16''
1-5/8''

3-1/4''
2-1/8''
3-3/4''

SPINDLE 8-3/4'' LONG (INCLUDING TENON)

3-7/16''

1''
3/4 x 3/4'' TENON (STUB)
2-1/4''
2-3/8''
3-5/8''
4-3/4''
4-3/8''

BASE

3/4 x 13/16'' MORTISE

USE THIS PATTERN to make candleholder shown in photos.

WEAR SAFETY GOGGLES

CUT VARIOUS segments to correct diameter using the parting tool.

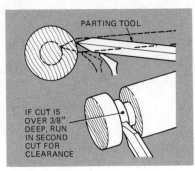

PARTING TOOL

IF CUT IS OVER 3/8'' DEEP, RUN IN SECOND CUT FOR CLEARANCE

HOLD PARTING tool 90° to work. Raise handle slightly as you push tool.

LAY OUT and cut groove for chimney using a small round-nose chisel.

PERIODICALLY check globe in the groove. Back off tailstock to do it.

NEXT, SHAPE the surface between the groove and the candle hole.

SHAPE COVE portion by working from both shoulders down to the center.

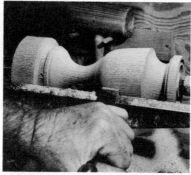

SKEW IN scraping attitude is an effective way to control shape.

SHARP GOUGE with shearing cut produced desirable results.

USING THE PARTING tool, make a cut to the desired tenon depth.

CHECK STUB diameter with caliper. When satisfied, turn to initial cut.

FILE, SUPPORTED by toolrest, is an excellent way to start smoothing.

FOR FINAL smoothing, use 220-grit paper (or emery cloth).

TO FINISH, remove the work from the lathe and bore the candle hole (or bore on the lathe with a chuck mounted in lathe) and cut off tenon on the bandsaw.

HOW TO GET A PROFESSIONAL FINISH

POUR A SMALL amount of shellac from a paper cup into a clean, lint-free cloth as a first step.

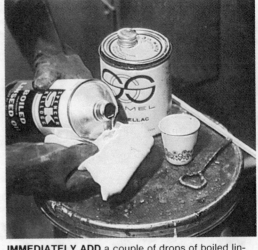

IMMEDIATELY ADD a couple of drops of boiled linseed oil to the shellac-dampened rag.

APPLY BY MOVING the rag across work with lathe at slow speed. Replenish the rag as needed.

APPLY RAG to all wide, easy-to-get-at surfaces on the cylinder's top and base.

TO WORK the finish into any crevices, wrap piece of rag around small-diameter stick.

REPEAT THE SAME procedure on the base; keep rag moving or you may create burn marks.

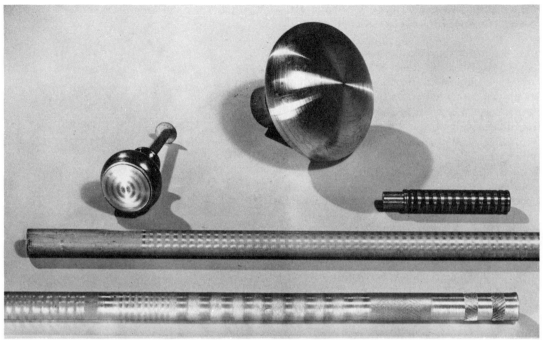

TYPICAL LATHE-PRODUCED FINISHES. Aluminum tubes were polished with abrasive rubber; their decorative bands were made with a knurler. Knobs were done with abrasive-rubber pencil or bit and abrasive cloth.

Put a fine finish on lathe projects

■ A COMPLETED SHOP PROJECT is generally rated by the appearance of its finish—the treatment applied to the surface to bring out its beauty and, perhaps, enhance its functional value. This can be particularly true when doing home shop lathe work on a model, a special tool or an instrument part.

There are so many ways of finishing turned metal that it's just about impossible to present them all in one article. But this abundance can be stimulating—it provides a lot of room for experimenting; you can enjoy the adventure of working out and trying other stunts on your own.

As a general rule, the type of finish to apply depends on the use to which the turned article is to be put. Roughly, some procedures can be grouped, as follows:

A SHARP TURNING TOOL used with a light touch produces smoothness. The lathe bit should have a rounded tip.

● *Turned finish.* For many purposes, as in making a punch for rough work, the finish left by the turning tool is good enough. A rounded tip is likely to produce a smoother finish-cut than a sharp, pointed tip. For the final, finishing pass, set the tool for a shallow cut and feed it very slowly along the work. Sulphurized oil or other lubricant may help. You'll find that the nature of the metal, as well as tool shape and sharpness, has a lot to do with the appearance of the turned surface.

Finish can be improved by using an oilstone (such as an Arkansas stone) to hone the cutting edge keen and smooth. *Tip*: If, when you attempt a very light cut, chatter develops and mars the turned surface, a switch to a lower spindle speed (even through back gears) may be a cure.

• *Filed finish*. When a turned surface isn't quite smooth enough, a bit of filing may be all that is needed. Although conventional files can be used on a lathe, steeper-toothed lathe files designed specifically for smoothing rotating work are better. Flat lathe files usually have untoothed edges. The work and file should be free of oil and other material, and the teeth kept clean by frequent brushing with a stiff wire brush. Bits of metal accumulating on and between file teeth can produce some unsightly grooves in the area being smoothed. Some mechanics rub a file with chalk to discourage chip pile-up. (When using a lathe file, take care to prevent fingers, sleeves and other parts of clothing from being snagged by the chuck, dog, or workpiece and always grip the file as if you are left-handed.)

• *Abrasive paper and cloth*. Coated abrasive materials include cloth and paper treated with aluminum oxide, silicon carbide, emery, crocus, or other abrasives such as grains or powders in various degrees of fineness. Grit size indicates the number of holes per inch in a sieve through which the grit will pass and may be expressed by that number, a fraction such as 4/0 or by an adjective such as "fine." You can use loose abrasive grit; there will be more on this later.

You often see emery cloth or paper recommended for polishing steel and other materials. (Emery, a natural variety of corundum, contains aluminum oxide and other minerals.) Probably some recommenders had in mind man-made aluminum oxide (such as Aloxite), or even silicon carbide (such as Carborundum) which is suitable for polishing hard, brittle materials. (Aluminum oxide seems preferable for tough steels and the like.)

One polishing procedure is to glue or staple a strip of the abrasive-coated material to a flat wooden stick, and use it like a file—dry or sulphurized, or with machine oil as with an oilstone.

Whether abrasive cloth, paper or loose grit or powder is used to smooth turned work, the accepted sequence is to start with a certain size grit (for example, medium No. 150, or 4/0) and proceed by steps to finer and finer sizes. The first

A FLAT FILE with its teeth cut at a sharper angle than a conventional file removes marks left by a turning tool.

ABRASIVE CLOTH mounted on a stick can be used for smoothing. Like a file, the abrasive should be kept moving.

A RIGID plastic-foam block, rubbed over a cake of buffing compound, provides an adequate sheen, too.

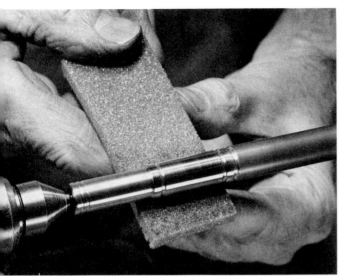

AN ABRASIVE-CHARGED foam pad is used to polish a brass rod after you smooth it with an abrasive cloth.

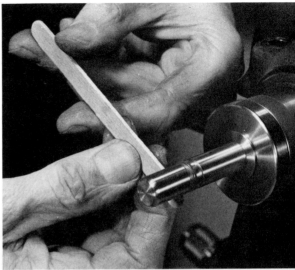

TIGHT GROOVES are polished with a flat stick charged with abrasive grit mixed with a light oil.

IMPORTED BUFFING POLISH, though intended for aluminum, works well on brass when applied with a cloth.

TO DEVELOP A LUSTER after polishing, use a piece of felt from an old hat to remove any dried compound.

grit polishes out tool or file marks; subsequent grits remove scratches caused by the proceeding, coarser grit. The second grit might be fine, No. 180 or 5/0, followed by extrafine, No. 220 or 6/0; and then finer polishing could be done with buffing compounds or commercial polishers. In the end, there may still be polishing scratches—but so fine they can't be seen without magnification.

The precise grit sizes to use can be found by trial. Usually, in home-shop work, a sufficiently smooth surface can be developed in two or three polishing steps.

A worthwhile economy in the shop is to never throw away a piece of abrasive cloth that still holds together. The longer it's used, the finer it cuts; eventually it may produce a shine equal to that from the finest new material.

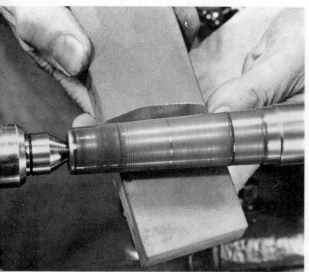

A TAPER is turned, using a flat oilstone lubricated with light oil. Move the oilstone in a back-and-forth motion.

A SMOOTH FINISH is given an oiled brass tubing with a diamond-tip grinding-wheel dresser used as a burnisher.

A HIGH-SPEED LATHE BIT can be used as a burnishing tool. Be sure that the work is kept well oiled.

A HAND-HELD KNURLING TOOL gives a fine, cross-hatched texture when held in the lathe.

Instead of a stick to support the abrasive cloth or paper, you can shape various blocks, pads of felt, plastic foam, leather and the like to polish rounded shapes, including grooves.

• *Buffing, honing, and burnishing.* Buffing removes flaws left by previous polishing. Buffing compounds usually consist of finely divided material mixed with a binder (dry powder in oil or other fluid). In normal lathe work, you probably would be more likely to buff brass, copper, aluminum or silver than steel.

A buffing compound designed for "cutting" is intended to be used first, followed by final buffing with a "coloring" preparation. Tripoli is a typical cutting material in buffing, while rouge (producing a burnishing rather than a cutting action) is used to bring out the final luster.

The buffing compound can be used on work spinning in a lathe by spreading it on a block or pad serving as the tool. The pad may be of leather, felt or plastic foam.

Of course, a piece can be polished on a con-

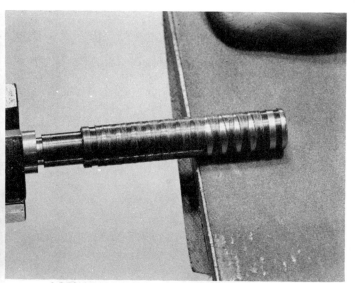

A DESIGN IS BIT-CUT in a blued-steel handle, and then polished with an abrasive cloth for a two-tone effect.

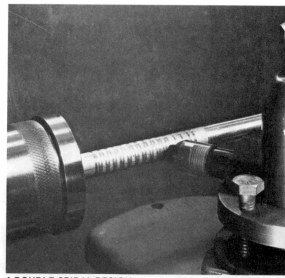

A DOUBLE-SPIRAL DESIGN was turned in aluminum by an abrasive-rubber pencil mounted as a "lathe tool."

ventional buffing wheel after removal from the lathe. Such a wheel, made of cloth or felt and charged with compound, might be mounted on a toolpost grinder and used to buff revolving work. Finally, buff with an uncharged wheel.

In oilstone lathe honing, an abrasive stone is held against the revolving work, primarily to grind down any metal points that might be projecting. Machine oil or special oilstone oil is the lubricant. The stone generally is moved back and forth parallel to the work axis, in circles or in figure-8s. "Superfinishing" is a form of honing with moving stones. Lathe headstock spindles operating in solid bearings are among parts on which superfinishing may be used.

Since a honed surface generally has a duller finish than a polished one, it can form a basis for subsequent polishing.

Lapping is an operation performed (often by hand rather than power) with abrasive grains plus oil or other fluid, to achieve close fitting of parts, bring gauges to precise size, even out surfaces and so on. Thus, you might lap a taper shank into a taper hole. Some lapping compounds are designed to break down readily to make their action self-limiting, and thus prevent "overlapping."

Lathe burnishing is simply a rubbing operation with a hard, highly polished tool pressed against the revolving, lubricated surface. Its desirability is best found by trial, for sometimes a similar smoothness can be produced readily by other methods. A sort of burnishing can be achieved with a diamond-point grinding-wheel dresser by adjusting it for light rubbing contact, employing fine feed and keeping the work well-oiled. But, some diamonds may prove too rough for a satisfactory result.

Sometimes the use of a commercial metal-polishing compound as a final finishing operation will develop on brass, aluminum, and the usual metals, a shine comparable to that achieved by wheelbuffing. Apply the polish to the spinning work with a small cloth or felt, manipulate the pad in contact for a while, then clean and polish with another cloth or felt. Always use a small cloth and check for roughness on the work that might snag it.

• *Texturing and "inlay" patterns*. Texturing consists of producing on the surface of turned work a pattern of lines or grooves that blend into a pleasing appearance. One way is to hand-hold a knurling tool lightly against the revolving work—preferably after polishing. Keep knurling pressure at a minimum, and frequently lift knurls from the surface and replace them, so they do

DECORATIVE CONCENTRIC RINGS are also produced by rubber. Space rings with the aid of a cross-feed scale.

COUNTLESS CONCENTRIC SCRATCHES made with abrasive-charged cloth give a starlike light reflection.

not tend to follow a repeat path (as would occur in conventional knurling).

For metal tool handles and levers to be grasped, an interesting, nonskid effect can be produced by first knurling or cross-threading the surface, blueing the piece if it is steel or applying colored lacquer if it is another metal, then filing and polishing it to remove color from the high spots while leaving it in depressions. Steel can be blued chemically or by heating until the desired oxide color develops.

● *Pattern polishing.* Selective polishing with an abrasive rubber eraser can produce interesting effects. The surface to be decorated should not be highly polished, but preferably a dull finish such as that developing on aluminum over a period of time.

Spiral patterns on cylindrical work can be produced by mounting the abrasive pencil like a regular lathe tool and using a coarse-thread setting, such as 4 t.p.i. (threads per inch), to control tool movement. Tracing right and left-hand overlapping "threads" produces a lattice effect. A series of bright bands or rings can be made with abrasive hand-held or in the toolpost.

By mounting the abrasive pencil as you would a conventional bit for a facing operation, you can produce concentric circles, spirals, or lattice designs on the flat surfaces or knobs, push plates and other items.

Those striking, circular-diffraction-grating-like effects you sometimes see on the front of transistor radios can be achieved on doorknobs,

push plates and the like by mounting the item on a lathe faceplate or in a chuck and holding against it, as it spins, a fine-grit abrasive paper or cloth or a felt pad charged with fine abrasive powder.

● *Loose abrasive grits.* Almost any abrasive, if finely divided, can be used for polishing lathe work. It's fun to try different materials—such as aluminum oxide or silicon carbide grains and powders, pumice, Damascus ruby powder, rottenstone, valve-grinding compound, various abrasives used by rockhounds—and even household cleaning materials. Generally you can mix the abrasive with oil and use it to charge a pad or stick held against the spinning work. It's a good idea, when using any abrasive that could fall on the lathe, to cover the carriage and bed.

● *Grinding.* A toolpost grinder can produce a smooth finish on both hardened and unhardened metal. While grinding is often used primarily to bring the work to a definite dimension, or work metal too hard to cut with tool bits, the proper abrasive wheel can produce a *very* smooth finish. Recommendations for wheel choice can be obtained from suppliers of grinding materials and equipment.

There exists a considerable array of materials for producing smoothness and brightness, or achieving novel effects. In many cases, the best way to find out what is most suited for the job is to do some experimenting—to polish or treat some scrap pieces before tackling the main one.

Filing on a lathe

AS YOUR LATHE FILING needs increase, you'll find your selection of lathe files growing to this size.

■ A FILE IS MORE than just a useful lathe tool. True, it will produce a fine finish—smoother, in fact, than that made by the turning tool. But it can also reduce a diameter by the merest fraction of an inch or millimeter—or it can rapidly cut down a shaft for a drive fit in a pulley or a running fit in a bearing.

In seconds, it can whack off the center tip left by a cutoff tool as shown in the photo below. It can make and smooth round, vee, or other odd-shaped grooves and fillets on turned work. A file can also serve as a miniature taper attachment for such operations as converting rod sections into taper pins, and it can quickly produce a neat point on punches and scribers. A pair of files can be manipulated to smooth and size simultaneously a small-diameter rod that's too limber for regular machining.

In fact, almost any type of file could be used in some form or other for lathe work. A common, single-cut, mill file can do a good job of smoothing turned work such as a shaft. Conventional three-square or triangular files are handy for touch-up work on small shoulders and grooves. For very fine finishes, or delicate shaping and sizing, Swiss-pattern files are often used. Even a conventional ignition file is handy where a thicker one would not do the job.

Thus, the lathe owner will indeed find it worthwhile to obtain one or more "lathe files." These are similar to conventional mill files, but their tooth angle is steeper, so that they cut with a more pronounced shearing action. This results in less clogging, smoother cutting, less chatter, more freedom from drag and faster cutting action—but they tend to crawl sidewise a bit more readily than a conventional file. On a sample mill file, the tooth angle (measured with respect to file length) was approximately 65°; tooth angles on similar lathe files are 45°.

Perhaps you can handle most of your routine lathe filing with as few as two files: a 10 or 12-in. lathe file for rapid, rough work, and an 8-in. lathe file for finishing. For greater all-around filing flexibility, however, you may want to supplement these with other files.

In oilstone lathe honing, an abrasive stone is held against the revolving work, primarily to grind down any metal points that might be projecting. Machine oil or special oilstone oil is the lubricant. The stone generally is moved back and forth parallel to the work axis, in circles or in figure-8s.

For a fine, *polished* finish, consider making an "abrasive file"—it's simply a strip of fine-grit or well-worn aluminum-oxide or silicon-carbide sheet abrasive. Tack or glue it to a flat wooden stick, or to a stick shaped for polishing contours.

Procedures for filing work in a lathe are not very complicated. The workpiece can be mounted in a chuck or collet, or between centers. If between centers, remember that filing friction can cause the workpiece to heat-expand lengthwise and bind on the centers. To prevent

SINCE FRICTION will heat the work and cause it to expand lengthwise, centers must be well lubricated.

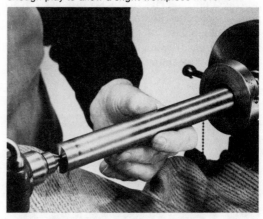

LATHE CENTERS should not be tight, but should have enough play to allow a slight workpiece movement.

A COARSE, FAST-CUTTING FILE can be used in the first stage of filing, keeping it at a right angle to the work.

FOR A FINELY POLISHED surface, an abrasive file can be made of a stick and strip of abrasive cloth.

this, put a little oil on the headstock center, and liberally lubricate the tailstock center. Then adjust center clearance so the workpiece can move freely.

Stop the lathe occasionally during prolonged filing and check for possible binding. If any squealing develops where the workpiece revolves on the tailstock center, stop the lathe immediately, loosen and relubricate.

For finish filing, run the lathe at a high speed—especially for any small-diameter work. But for simply filing off a sharp edge or tip, normal turning speed will do.

With smooth, even and medium-pressure strokes, keep the file moving across the revolving work. Normally you should hold the file square with the work axis, or nearly so. You may find, however, that a smoother overall finish results if you move the file in a slightly diagonal path.

If the file begins to lose its bite, or if it tends to skip or cause streaks on the work, clean the teeth with a file card or small wire-bristle, suede-shoe brush.

Although file technicians suggest that the surface be oil-free, you may find that a sulphurized cutting oil or similar fluid can be helpful. When filing a rusty shaft, a dash of cutting oil will minimize nose-irritating dust and also reduce the depositing of filings on the lathe bed and carriage. A sulphurized cutting oil I used on various occasions seemed not to decrease the files' efficiency, and perhaps it tended to reduce tooth wear. But because the oil does hold filings in the teeth, the accumulations had to be wiped off after just several strokes of the file.

Regular lathe files have "safe" edges—that is, the edges are smooth, without teeth. The file thus can be used close to a chuck or other part without tending to bite into it. If you use conven-

SMALL SWISS-PATTERN FILES are handy for shaping and smoothing small parts. In the photo below a dimpling punch is being used for this purpose.

DISC-SHAPED SECTIONS where a precise radius is not required can be both shaped and finished with files. As shown here, the file is hand-held.

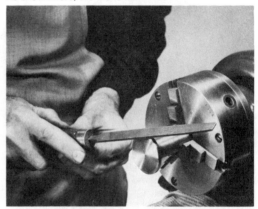

GROOVED SECTIONS can be made or smoothed by using an appropriately shaped Swiss-pattern file. If you do much fine work, you'll want to purchase a set.

AN EASY-TO-MAKE GUIDE helps control the depth of degree of filing. This kind of guide is especially handy for producing bullet or dome shapes.

tional files lacking such safe edges, be careful that the edge doesn't touch any moving surface. One practice is to grind toothed edges smooth before attempting to do lathe filing.

When filing work that is revolving in a lathe, use sensible safety precautions. Hold the file firmly, and be careful that it does not catch on the workpiece to be tossed your way, or become entangled with a chuck.

It's always a good idea not to stand directly in line with the file handle. When you reach over the lathe to grasp the outer end of the file, be careful not to be grabbed by the chuck or dog. On your forearms, wear tight-fitting sleeves or, better yet, none at all.

The life of a lathe file can be greatly reduced by improper care or carelessness. Never throw a file into a drawer or toolbox—also avoid stacking them on top of one another. Instead, always keep them separate by hanging them in a rack placed out of the way so they won't be knocked off accidentally and damaged.

Before storing the file, however, make certain that all chips have been brushed out of the file ridges. If oil or grease is left on the file, it can be removed by wiping with a soft clean cloth, then rubbing chalk into the file teeth. A soft iron "pick" should also be kept on hand for removing troublesome filings that may become imbedded in the teeth.

FILING ATTACHMENTS and accessories include a filing guide and two-file assembly for thin limber rods.

A DOUBLE-FILE ASSEMBLY should be used at high speed. The cutting pressure is set by squeezing the open end to produce the desired diameter.

A SIMPLE BALL-TURNING GAUGE can be formed from a suitable washer, then used to check the ball diameter. Continue until you get a snug fit.

WEAR SAFETY GOGGLES

Turn plastic on your lathe

■ IF YOU'RE WEARY of turning steel and brass on your home-shop lathe, you can find diversion and challenge in working with an interesting nonmetal material—rigid PVC (poly-vinyl chloride). It comes in various forms including sheet, pipe and fittings. In addition, there are other plastics rigid enough to be machined—such as acrylics (Plexiglas).

Shapes readily handled on the lathe, which can be used as good starting points in making various items, include pieces of rigid plastic pipe and such items as couplings, male and female adapters, cleanout plugs and fittings. Many local building-supply stores handle them, sometimes in a choice of colors such as white, gray, and ivory. Also, local distributors and fabricating shops often can provide sheet stock and scrap pieces of plastic materials they handle.

From such odds and ends, you can make various ornaments and novelties; even useful items such as washers and shade pulls. Or a trivet or trinket box (made from a Tepco fitting and plug) as shown in the drawing that follows. The photos show a few lathe-turned items produced from random plastic parts (mostly of rigid PVC) found at local stores and in a shop scrapbox.

In production machining of rigid plastic materials, specially sharpened tools often are used. Some plastic compounds are so abrasive that tungsten-carbide tools are needed. But for limited machining of rigid PVC on a home-shop lathe, tools normally used for metals will do.

First, in turning plastics be sure that the work-piece is securely mounted in the lathe—that

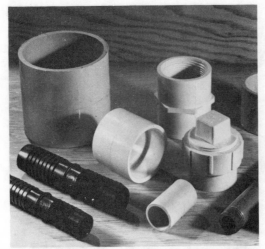

STOCK ITEMS are easily handled on lathe. Two black couplings in foreground fit plastic pipe.

TO PREVENT WALLS from being crushed, cut a plug from ¾-in. plywood to fit pipe's inside diameter.

USE PARTING or grooving bit to cut decorative grooves in future jewel box.

REMOVAL IS EASIER if all but a few turns of threads at top are machined off jewel-box cover.

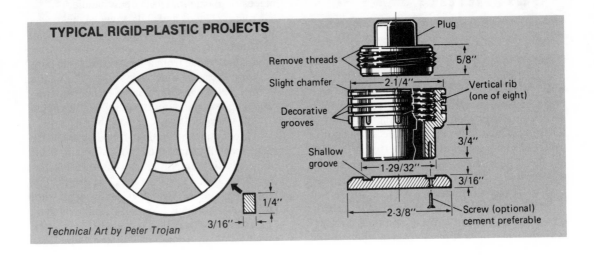

TYPICAL RIGID-PLASTIC PROJECTS

Plug

Remove threads

5/8"

Slight chamfer

2-1/4"

Vertical rib (one of eight)

Decorative grooves

3/4"

Shallow groove

1-29/32"

3/16"

1/4"

3/16"

2-3/8"

Screw (optional) cement preferable

Technical Art by Peter Trojan

CUT BOTTOM FOR BOX from sheet plastic using a cutoff tool. Next, cut scrap away by hand.

FASTEN DISC to the chucked wooden mandrel using contact cement with a piece of paper between.

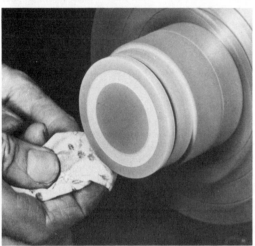

TO POLISH DISC, use a soft rag and non-abrasive cleansing powder. Groove receives round wall.

AS YOU DRILL HOLE in the end of the cast-resin rod, chips are almost white—though rod is amber color.

PLASTIC COUPLING of the type used to join flexible plastic pipe is soft but still machinable.

IN THREADING END of rigid PVC pipe, with aid of a center rest, use regular threading tool.

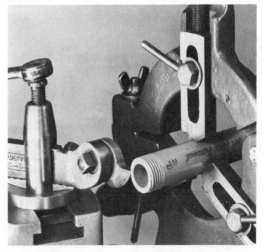

chuck jaws grip it firmly and that there is no unsupported overhang that is likely to cause trouble. Keep cutting tools sharp. Until you get the "feel" of the material and operation, it's good to use slow spindle speeds and a careful feed. Then judge whether you will gain by increasing speed and feed. Don't let chips accumulate.

In doing the work illustrated, ordinary lathe tools ground for machining brass and steel were used and worked well. Edges were kept keen by frequent honing. Tools generally were set with cutting edges in line with the workpiece center, as in threading. Those ground with zero or slightly negative rake and plenty of clearance seemed to work well in many cases.

In cutting the key-chain links with a thin-blade parting tool, the lathe was run at the lowest of its four direct (nonback-geared) spindle speeds. This produced free-flowing chips and a cut surface having a good finish that required little further treatment other than knocking off sharp edges.

Chips often come from the tool in long, uncurled ribbons and may collect in loose bunches which have to be cleared at intervals. Chips from any plastic accumulating on or near the lathe should be removed frequently. Besides being messy, they might be a fire hazard. If the plastic produces a nose-irritating dust, use a breathing mask.

Some stringy chips may wind around the work, like thread on a spool, and have to be removed when they become a nuisance by obscuring the cut or tool. When rounding sharp edges with a file (single-cut files are preferred), a by-product may be very fine, clinging "whiskers." To rub them off, hold a piece of felt against the revolving work. All lathe work on the items in the photos was done without use of cutting fluid.

Mounting work in lathe

Under chuck-jaw pressure, a tubular piece can distort so readily that it is impossible to get a firm bite on it. A remedy is to insert a wooden plug in the end gripped by the chuck. For a large diameter, this can be a disc of ½ to ¾-in. plywood jigsawed or turned to a light drive fit. For a small pipe or tube, a dowel may do. Rigid plastic materials can be marred by rough chuck (or vise) jaws; a layer or two of masking tape or other padding around the outside diameter where the jaws will bite is advisable.

Unsupported projection of a workpiece from a chuck should be kept as small as feasible. For threading and other operations near the ends of somewhat long tubes, rods and pipe sections, a center rest with jaws as near the outer end as possible is a good bet. Tubes and pipe sections can be center-supported like rods if their inside diameter is not greater than the diameter of the pointed portion of the center; or they can be plugged and mounted between centers, like metal rods. Centers are lubricated with oil.

Corners, edges and surfaces can be smoothed with fine abrasive sheet. The degree of polish obtainable is best found by tests on the material being worked. Some plastics will require more polishing to bring out a desirable sheen. Merely burnishing with a wooden stick or one charged with an abrasive may be sufficient; this is one way of smoothing bottoms of deep grooves and the like. Non-abrasive cleaning powder on a cloth or felt pad will polish some plastics spinning on a lathe; it was used for the base of the trinket box shown. Other polishes, such as those for brass or aluminum, could be tried. It's fun to experiment on scrap with various abrasives.

Decorating plastic

Finished plastic can be decorated with paints or lacquers. Hobby shops usually carry paints for the plastic-model trade. A gold paint was used in the grooves turned on the trinket box.

An attempt to knurl a rigid PVC pipe resulted in a shallow pattern consisting essentially of grooves in cross-hatch arrangement. The material tended to give under knurl pressure, and well-formed diamonds could not be produced. However, the resulting diamond-hatch of lines was attractive and could serve as a slip-resistant grip surface.

Off-the-lathe treatment of turned items may include cutting, drilling, boring, milling, filing, bending and cementing. In the home shop, rigid PVC can be worked successfully enough with ordinary on-hand, "nonlathe" tools intended for wood or metal. For hand-sawing, try a dovetail saw or small hacksaw; for splitting rings to make the key chain, a jeweler's saw is preferable.

Because rigid PVC is not a good thermal conductor, the frictional heat generated by drilling or another operation may build up rapidly in a tool. Drill bits and other cutters should be watched for signs of overheating. As suggested earlier, tools should be sharp so that they produce less friction. Plastics containing fillers dull edges rapidly. A drill bit may seem to cut easily and penetrate with little resistance, but it should

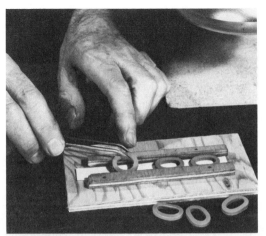

ELONGATED LINKS were formed by heating with lamp, then letting them cool between wood strips.

GROOVES can be cut in plastic using lathe as shaper. Here cross-slide is moved to and fro while side-mounted cutoff bit plows grooves in edge.

EXAMPLES of lathe-turned plastic: Black couplings were machined to slide together like telescope tube; trinket box was made from cleanout plug; oversize key chain is of two diameters of rigid pipe.

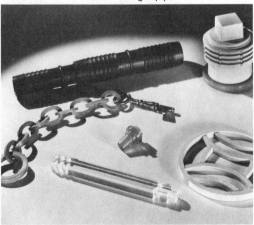

be withdrawn frequently, especially from a deep hole, for cooling and chip removal. Well-polished bit flutes offer less resistance.

For a threaded hole in a plastic material, you may use a slightly larger drill than for metal, to prevent excessive thread height. When there is a great deal of threading to be done, you may grind the tap (or die) teeth to a slightly negative front-angle rake.

If necessary, a plug can be installed to stiffen the wall of a pipe or tube for lathe-threading. Such threading may weaken the material; if the wall is thin, joining parts with cement generally is preferable. Suitable cements are sold by sources of rigid pipe and fittings.

Shaping with heat

Rigid PVC, a thermoplastic material, can be heat-softened. In its soft state, it can be bent, stretched or otherwise modified; upon returning to room temperature, it will be rigid again. For example, rings cut from a rigid Koroseal pipe for making the oversize key chain shown were softened by placing them a few inches from a 250-w. reflector heat lamp for a minute or so. Then they were made into elongated links by squeezing them between two parallel wooden strips. Alternate links were split with a jeweler's saw, snapped through adjacent links, and rejoined by cementing.

Softened PVC should be handled carefully so that its surface is not damaged; if cooled against a rough board it may show the embossed texture of the board surface.

Though rigid PVC was used mostly in the sample projects, other plastics can be worked on a lathe, among them cast or molded resins. Some tough, somewhat softer plastics, such as those used for couplings for bendable polyethylene pipe, can be machined, but you may have to guard against a tendency for them to bend too readily. PVC stock pieces may vary in properties; there are extra-rigid grades for severe service. When turning such materials, the lathe operator usually has little difficulty in detecting differences in their response to tool action.

But whatever the particular piece of PVC or other plastic, it is interesting to determine what can be done with it on a lathe. The venture can be useful, for rigid plastic parts, besides being somewhat easier to obtain and easier to machine than metal ones, may have certain properties that no metal can boast—such as a desirable resistance to oils, grease, water, weather, as well as most chemicals likely to be encountered.

Turning rings on a lathe

■ RINGMAKING IS an exciting but often overlooked talent of the metal-working lathe. You can turn out sizes and shapes you could never buy—big, little, square, rectangular, triangular, oval, round, half-round, hexagonal, octagonal—you name it. You can make them of steel, cast iron, brass, aluminum, rigid plastic, even hardwood such as maple.

Turned rings are, of course, jointless. They have a handsome, elegant look that makes them ideal for pieces of jewelry and ornamental hardware. They can be used as decorative drawer and cabinet pulls, ladies' brooches and stands for models. Large rings can serve as bracelets or unusual picture frames.

The stock you use for making rings can be hollow tubing or pipe or solid bar material in round, hexagonal or other shapes. If you start with bar stock, you first bore out the center. Plain rings can be made simply by slicing sections off your stock like cutting a loaf of bread. If the width of the slice is the same as the wall thickness of your stock, you have a ring of square cross section. By making cuts at various angles, you end up with a ring of triangular, diamond, hexagonal or octagonal section.

As a matter of safety, it is not a good idea to let the stock project excessively beyond the chuck. The shorter the projection, the better. Chuck jaws can grip a tubular piece on either the outside or inside. Sometimes the outer end of a solid bar can be steadied on a tailstock center if you don't bore away the material at the bar's center until later.

Support and secure workpiece

When rings are to be cut from long stock, the piece should be supported near its outer end by a steady rest, as shown in some of the photos. The end toward the headstock should be gripped firmly by the chuck or lashed securely to the faceplate to prevent endwise crawl from occurring.

Single rings often are clamped in a chuck for minor finishing operations such as filing or sanding for smoothness, rounding sharp edges, or removing the "flash" left by a cut-off tool. The ring should be clamped to run true. Sometimes an independent-jaw chuck is preferable because the ring can be centered accurately with the aid of a gauge.

Remember that when you clamp a ring in a chuck, jaw pressure springs it slightly out of round. Tubular stock is similarly distorted near the chuck. A ring machined from a blank distorted in this way will not be perfectly circular when jaw pressure is released. In most cases, this is probably not important, but it could affect ring fit in close-tolerance work, such as in making optical-instrument parts.

PLASTIC RING, turned from a section of plastic plumbing pipe, gets a polishing below before final cut is made to separate it from the remaining stock.

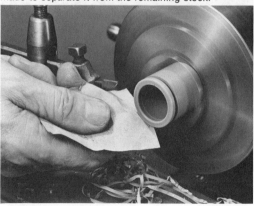

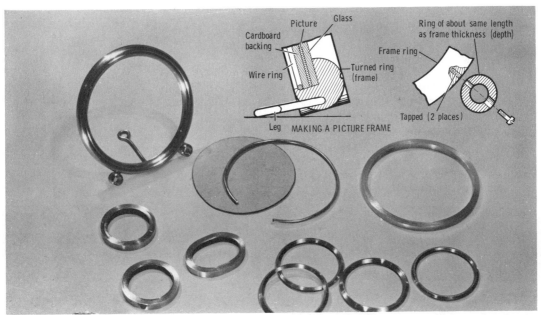

MAKING A PICTURE FRAME

SOME OF THE MANY rings you can make are shown above. The oval ring to the left of center was made by squeezing a round ring with pliers to flatten it slightly. At the top of the photo is an example of how a large ring can become a decorative picture frame. A recess is machined at the back to hold the picture and the legs are added as shown in the sketch. Big rings of this type could also make interesting and novel ladies' bracelets.

Some of the Many Different Shapes You Can Make

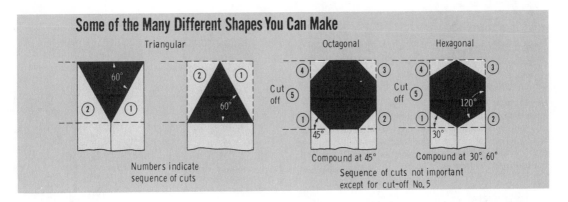

RINGS DROP OFF one after another and slide neatly onto this automatic catcher. The simple device consists of a bent wire held in the tailstock chuck.

FREEHAND TURNING enables you to shape round, oval and other curved-section rings. The tool is handheld. A bar clamped in the toolpost serves as a toolrest.

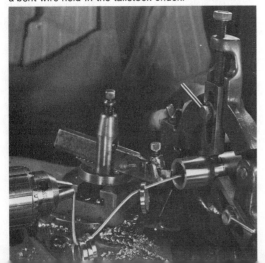

Metal, plastic and wood rings can be shaped freehand on a metal lathe in much the same manner as parts are formed on a wood-turning lathe, the tool being handheld and supported by a fixed rest.

Carbide-tipped turning chisels are available for use on metal parts, or you can grind suitable ones from tool steel or high-speed-steel lathe bits. Various common wood-turning chisel shapes are useful in working metal rings. The skewer shape is particularly handy. Such tools can be manipulated to cut, rather than scrape, metal neatly from the work, with the formation of fine, thin chips. The hand-turning technique is

HOMEMADE BITS speed the work on special jobs, such as turning out round or oval-section rings in quantity. The one below, for round-section rings, was made from an old file. Two holes of ring diameter were drilled, the material between them removed, relief angles filled, and the tool was rehardened. The bit is held in a regular boring-bar holder as shown above.

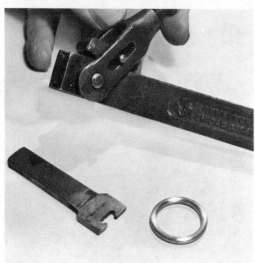

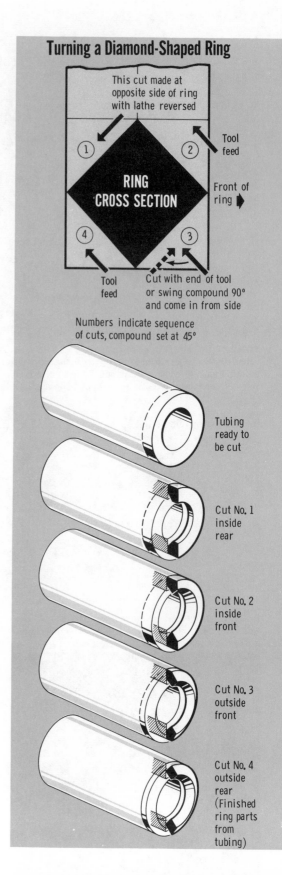

Turning a Diamond-Shaped Ring

This cut made at opposite side of ring with lathe reversed

Tool feed

Front of ring ➤

RING CROSS SECTION

① ② ④ ③

Tool feed

Cut with end of tool or swing compound 90° and come in from side

Numbers indicate sequence of cuts, compound set at 45°

Tubing ready to be cut

Cut No. 1 inside rear

Cut No. 2 inside front

Cut No. 3 outside front

Cut No. 4 outside rear (Finished ring parts from tubing)

INSIDE CUT on diamond-shaped ring is made at far side of stock with lathe reversed. All other cuts are made at stock's near side.

OUTER CORNER can be removed in two ways. You can feed toward headstock, as here, using square end of bit, or swing compound 90° and feed from opposite.

INNER lip of stock is machined by feeding tool with compound-slide screw. Final cut has been started here, will be deepened later to part ring.

useful in shaping rings having round, oval, or similar cross section and in making decorative grooves and ridges.

Rings having diamond-shaped, triangular, hexagonal and octagonal sections can be formed by feeding the tool with the compound rest set at the proper angle. Here is a helpful way to work out the machining sequence: Draw a scaled plan of the desired ring cross section, showing it as if you were looking down on top with the side facing you representing the side toward which the tool will feed. With this, you can easily determine the angles, dimensions of various faces, and distances the tool must travel in making different cuts. These values are then used to control the movement of the tool bit by means of the micrometer collars on the carriage screws, particularly that controlling the compound slide.

Numbers indicate cutting sequence

The drawings show the cross-sectional layout of rings of various sections. The numbered segments indicate waste material to be machined away. In some cases, the numbers represent a suggested cutting sequence, selected to make it easier to establish starting points for measuring tool movement.

You can make nonmetal rings from such materials as rigid PVC (polyvinyl chloride) pipe available in many stores. Such plastic material is machined much as if it were metal. It is easy to cut and requires only moderate tool pressure. Chuck-jaw pressure should be controlled according to the strength and bendability of the material.

A ring can be machined to serve as a frame for a round picture, plaque or other object. In the back of the frame, machine a recess to receive the picture, a glass or plastic cover if one is used and a piece of backing material, such as heavy cardboard. The simplest holding arrangement consists of an open ring of wire sprung into a shallow groove around the inside of the recess. Feet for the frame to stand on can be made from smaller rings attached to the main ring with screws, rivets or solder.

Finishing the rings

You can finish turned rings in the same way as other items of the same materials. Files and abrasive paper or cloth are suitable for smoothing most materials. Rings can be given various distinctive textures by knurling them while they are in the lathe, or by some other suitable treatment such as peening, engraving or stamping.

Lawn care for the best lawn in your neighborhood

■ THE NO. 1 PROBLEM of most lawns is not scraggly weeds, grasping crabgrass or hungry insects. The No. 1 problem is human nature.

Come spring, most homeowners can hardly wait to get in the warm sun and begin rolling the still-soggy turf, reseeding bare spots, spreading fertilizer, and swinging the first punch at crabgrass. Their enthusiasm carries into summer.

But come fall, most homeowners have had it.

Mowing has become a tiresome chore, and crabgrass is fighting back. Besides, there are storm windows to hang and the kids are beginning to ask for help with their homework. Suddenly it's much easier to forget everything that needs to be done, including lawn work.

Yet fall is the prime time for renovating a lawn. A little work invested then will pay off in a vastly improved lawn the next year. Lawn care is a round-the-calendar operation, but fall offers real opportunity.

• Nature is shedding seeds herself, and offers a big boost to your own efforts.

• Grass has come out of its summer dormancy and is growing vigorously in an unconscious urge to prepare itself for winter.

• Weeds are again growing vigorously, and thus are prime targets for weed killers. If you kill weeds in spring and summer, the resulting bare spots are likely to be infested with an even worse enemy—crabgrass. If you kill weeds in the fall, crabgrass has begun to go dormant, and fine grasses will spread to fill bare spots.

Furthermore, seedlings established in the fall are much more likely to survive. Heat, not cold, is the biggest environmental threat to a seedling. If you reseed in the spring, some of your tender new plants will inevitably be killed by summer heat and drought; on the other hand, if you sow seed in early fall, seedlings will be well established by the time they are covered with an insulating blanket of snow, and will emerge healthy and vigorous in the spring, when they will have three or four months to mature before they are exposed to the summer sun.

Autumn may be the best time to give your lawn rehabilitation treatment, but you don't have to wait until then to start applying good practices. You may be able to improve its health considerably by changing your mowing or watering habits, or by feeding it now. And if the weeds are using it for a picnic ground, you can dampen their enthusiasm now—and totally wipe them out later.

There is no such thing as the perfect all-around grass. If there were, it would be disease-free in all situations, would grow in all parts of the country, thrive in both the sun and the shade, survive long droughts, and put up with constant trampling. Alas, the best we can do is to select the best grass for each situation.

The grasses which do best in the southern states are quite different from the stellar performers of the north and northwest. Check the **map below** for the best grasses for your area. As a rule, dealers feature seeds and mixtures tailored for the local climate.

Read the labels as you shop. These days they tell you a lot. And look for "mixtures." These are formulations of four to six different grasses put together by seed companies to give you the best possible combination of grasses.

The box will list any type of seed present in excess of five percent. Beware of mixtures containing very high percentages of annual grasses, usually annual ryes. These won't grow the second year. Their chief value is that they germinate quickly and serve to shelter the slower-starting perennials during the early weeks after seeding. This is important if you are sowing a new lawn, but of little value if you are reseeding an old one.

The label also shows the amount of weed seed present in the mixture. Compare labels and look for the lowest amount of weed seed and the highest amount of perennial grass seed. You'll pay more for the better mixtures, but you buy more good grass and less weed grief when you do.

Always buy fresh seed. When grass seed is on sale, find out why the price has been cut. Perhaps the dealer wants to attract new customers, which is a legitimate reason—or perhaps he wants to move some older seed, which isn't good. The reason is that the older the seed, the less of it you can expect to germinate.

The label gives you two important clues to the freshness of the seed and its ability to germinate. The first is the figure showing the percentage of germination of each seed in the mixture. This tells you how viable the seed was at the time of testing. Good seed runs 88 percent or better.

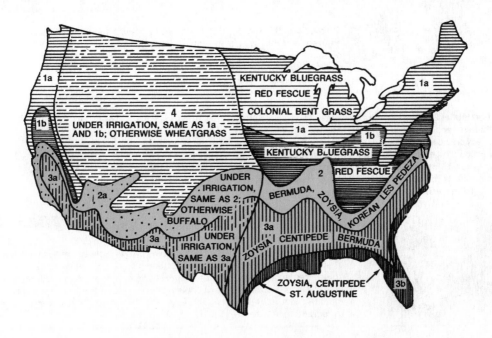

ARE YOU MISTREATING YOUR LAWN?

PROBLEM LAWNS have become problems in most cases because they are mistreated. Over many years, experts have found that most problems are caused by a standard group of errors. If you have a tired, disloyal lawn, you probably are committing one or more of these seven sins.

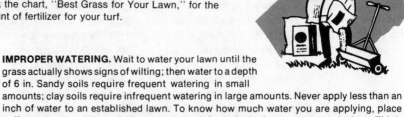

IMPROPER USE OF FERTILIZER. Too little nitrogen starves your lawn; too much weakens the root structure. See the section on feeding your lawn and also check the chart, "Best Grass for Your Lawn," for the recommended amount of fertilizer for your turf.

IMPROPER WATERING. Wait to water your lawn until the grass actually shows signs of wilting; then water to a depth of 6 in. Sandy soils require frequent watering in small amounts; clay soils require infrequent watering in large amounts. Never apply less than an inch of water to an established lawn. To know how much water you are applying, place coffee cans around the sprinkled area and wait for an inch of water to appear in them. This is the minimum amount. If you live in Area 1A (see map), your lawn won't stay green in midsummer even if you water as directed, because virtually all cool-season grasses go dormant in midsummer. They'll turn green again in the fall.

POOR SEED MIXTURES. Buy only seed that is fresh and that is right for your area. Read "How to Buy Seed" and don't try to save money on cheap mixes which contain undesirable seed types. Check the germination data and the seed formula on the box.

POOR MOWING PRACTICES. Don't mow too low because when you do you don't leave enough leaf area to provide for good root development. Never remove more than half the blade at one time. See recommended mowing heights on the chart.

TOO MUCH TRAFFIC. Most of us believe that lawns should be played on and enjoyed, and normal activity won't harm a good lawn. But heavy traffic in certain areas, particularly during the winter and early spring, compacts the soil so it can no longer support grass. Don't fight the system. Pave or lay stone in areas which always get heavy traffic.

TOO MUCH SHADE. Most grasses are not adapted to shady areas, and those that are recommended for shade still must get some sun. To help grass in shady areas, fertilize frequently but lightly. Prune tree branches when possible to allow a bit more light through. Then fertilize the trees four to five ft. deep so they won't steal food from the grass, and apply lime to the shaded soil, which is more likely to become acid. Finally, remove leaves and clippings frequently from these areas.

POORLY DRAINED SOILS. Grass plants will drown in those depressed areas of your lawn where water gathers in puddles. Soil in these areas becomes compacted quickly, too. Fill these depressions with layers of top soil added a little at a time. Slopes also are a problem because the water runs off so quickly that the grass gets little water. There also may be erosion. The best solution is to regrade the lawn.

The second clue is the date of the germination test. The law requires that the seed be shipped within five months of the test. Reputable seed companies are careful to replace aging stocks in stores—but check the date anyway. If several brands are available, check one against the other and buy the freshest. More of it will sprout.

You'll find two basic types of mixtures, one for a beautiful "picture" front lawn, and another for play areas which receive rough wear. The show lawn has fine-bladed grasses which produce a lawn of exceptional color and texture. The play grasses are tougher, broader-bladed, and not as deep a green.

If you always believed that rye grass was a poor lawn grass, you must now change your mind. The old ryes were wide-bladed, coarse annual grasses. The new turf-type ryes are perennials which mix well with bluegrass. They were bred especially for soft fibers, to provide clean cutting. Common rye, when mowed, gets frayed ends which turn brown. The new ryes cut as nicely as bluegrass, with no browning, and their fine blades don't give the lawn a coarse look.

You'll also find a variety of seed mixtures tailored for sowing in shady places—but don't be misled. All grasses need some sun. The more dense your shade, the less likely you are to grow grass. Shady lawn mixtures actually are for lawns which receive partial or filtered sunlight. They will grow where bluegrass won't, but they won't grow without some sun.

Finally, when shopping for grass seed, keep an eye open for new varieties. A lot of research is being carried on to develop new types of grasses, for the seed producers are still searching for the perfect grass. Read the labels and literature carefully, to find out what improvements the new seed offers. Expect such features as better resistance to disease, richer color, better drought or shade survival, or the ability to form a more dense turf in a single growing season.

Feeding your lawn

To have a healthy lawn which grows vigorously, has rich color, and renews itself, you need to see that its grasses get enough nourishment. This means that you must make periodic applications of fertilizer. But not just any fertilizer. The element which makes grass greener, promotes good growth, and helps to build roots is nitrogen—so the fertilizer must be rich in nitrogen.

Most soils have too little nitrogen, and when you apply it to the soil in any form, the nitrogen washes out in time. This is why continued applications are necessary. The amount of nitrogen needed varies with the type of grass. Common Kentucky bluegrass and fescues need about 3 pounds per 1000 square feet of lawn per year. Some of the improved bluegrasses need 5 pounds. Bent grass needs about 4 pounds.

You can feed two or three times a year, applying about 1 pound of nitrogen per 1000 square feet each time. After the long winter, your grass

---

YOUR LAWN-CARE CALENDAR
(For regions 1A, 1B and most of region 4. Warm-season grasses grown
in regions 2 and 3 require care only during the hot summer months.)

Early fall—If your lawn needs a complete renovation, do it now (see separate section). Apply herbicide to eliminate broadleaf weeds. Apply lime if needed. In September, apply half of your fall fertilizer allotment. Rake bare areas and reseed; water lightly but often.

Late fall—In mid-October, apply the other half of the fall fertilizer allotment. Continue mowing as long as the grass grows; do not leave the grass 'tall for the winter months. Mulch the leaves as they fall, or if they tend to clot on the lawn, rake and remove them.

Early spring—Rake trash from lawn. Apply lime if needed, and if you were too lazy to do it last fall. Apply a pre-emergent crabgrass killer. In late February or early March, spread a light application of fertilizer, or a heavier application of slow-release fertilizer. Reseed any bare spots you missed last

fall. If the soil has heaved from frost, use a light roller but not a heavy one. Apply a herbicide for chickweed if that weed is a problem in your lawn.

Late spring—Give your lawn another light shot of fertilizer. Kill the broadleaf weeds. Mow according to the recommended practice for your type of grass. You should have used a pre-emergent crabgrass killer months ago. If you didn't, do it now.

Summer—If you have a zoysia or Bermuda-grass lawn, feed it in July and again in August. Mow frequently enough that you remove no more than one-half the total leaf length. If you have a bluegrass lawn, don't worry if it turns brown—it's dormant as nature intended it to be. In long periods of drought, water deeply once a week. Take a vacation. When you return, if the grass is so long that the clippings may smother the lawn, remove them as you mow.

is hungry and active in the spring—and so should be fed in April. It grows vigorously until early June (early July for improved bluegrasses), and takes a nap until September, when it wakes up and starts feeding for the winter ahead. Experts advise feeding the second meal around the first of June, just before nap time. They tell you not to feed in July or August unless you have a bent grass lawn, which could use a snack about the first of August.

The big, important meal comes in the fall—anytime in September. If you cut out any feeding, skip the June application. But don't miss the fall feeding, whatever else you do. This is the one which determines how strong your lawn will be next spring.

Now—about buying your fertilizer—there have been so many claims and counterclaims about lawn foods that most homeowners are confused. They buy bags of anything labeled as great for lawns, without thinking about nutritional values. And often they spend unnecessary money doing it this way.

A complete fertilizer contains three elements: nitrogen, for stimulating leaf growth; phosphorous, for the formation of strong roots; and potash, to give plants stamina and disease resistance. Every bag of fertilizer is labeled with the percentages of these elements it contains. Thus, a 10-6-4 fertilizer consists of 10 percent available nitrogen, 6 percent phosphorous, 4 percent potash—and 80 percent inert carrying material.

Since nitrogen is the most vital of these elements, and also the most expensive, the *first* figure on the label is the one which you should pay most attention to. Simply divide this figure by 100. The answer is the number of pounds of fertilizer you must buy to apply 1 lb. of nitrogen to 1000 sq. ft. of lawn; it's a good idea not to apply more than 1 pound of nitrogen per 1000 sq. ft. of established lawn at any one time.

You can buy organic or inorganic fertilizer. Organic fertilizers are processed from such plant or animal materials as sewage sludge and bonemeal. Soil bacteria cause them to break down and release nutrients into the soil. Their action is slower, and during decomposition they become a part of the soil.

Inorganic fertilizers, urea-form and resin-form mixtures, are synthetic fertilizers which slowly release nitrogen into the soil as a result of rain and moisture. They begin feeding quickly, which is an advantage, but it is easy to overfeed a lawn with these. Overstimulation causes spindly top growth and weakens the lawn. Plan your feed-

NAME	GEOGRAPHICAL AREA
1. KENTUCKY BLUEGRASS	
Common	1A, 1B, 4 under irrigation
Merion	1A, 1B, northern 2
Park	1A, 1B
2. RED FESCUES	
Common	1A
Pennlawn	1A
3. ASTORIA	1B
4. ZOYSIAS	
Meyer	southern 1A, northern 2
Emerald	2
Manilagrass	2
5. BERMUDAGRASSES	
Everglades 1	southern 2
Ormond	southern 2
Texturf 10	2 and 3 in Texas
Tifgreen	2, 3
Tiflawn	2
6. ST. AUGUSTINES	
Floratine	2
Bitter blue	2
7. BAHIAGRASS	2
8. CENTIPEDE	2
9. BUFFALOGRASS	southern 4
10. BLUE GRAMA	4
11. WHEATGRASS	northern 4

ings with these materials carefully.

The chart shows various combinations of inorganic fertilizers as well as some of the more common organic materials. It indicates how much total fertilizer you have to buy to apply 1 lb. of nitrogen per 1000 sq. ft. of your lawn.

When buying any kind of fertilizer, don't shop for the lowest-priced bag on display, because in use its contents may actually be the most expensive. Fifty pounds of one fertilizer may be needed to provide 1 lb. of fertilizer for a 2000-sq.-ft. lawn, while 100 pounds of a cheaper fertilizer may be needed. Be a smart buyer and do a quick computation. Divide 100 into the nitrogen number on the bag—and then compare prices. You may find that a $9 bag is cheaper than a $6 one because the $9 bag puts a pound of nitrogen on more square feet.

HERE YOU'LL FIND THE BEST GRASS FOR YOUR LAWN

CHARACTERISTICS	MOWING HEIGHT	BEST SEEDING OR PLANTING TIME	NITROGEN, LBS./ 1000 SQ. FT. ANNUALLY
Excellent cool-area grass; withstands abuse; not good for heavy shade.	1½-2"	Fall	3-4
Low-growing, short leaves, good color; thick turf; leaf-spot-resistant.	1½-2"	Fall	6-8
Vigorous and resistant to rust, particularly in far north.	1½-2"	Fall	3-4
More tolerant of shade than bluegrass, narrow leaf, good color.	1-2"	Fall	2-3
Better turf than common red fescues, more tolerant of leaf spot.	1-2"	Fall	2-3
Beautiful bentgrass lawn, but requires continuous and expensive care.	¾" or less	Fall	4-6
Dense turf able to withstand hot, humid summer.	¾-1"	Spring	5-10
Dense, relatively weed-free turf. Very slow to establish.	¾-1"	Spring	5-10
Very dense, stands considerable shade.	¾-1"	Spring	5-10
Dark green, fine textured, vigorous; excellent for Florida.	¾-1"	Spring	5-10
Blue-green, slow growing; resists leaf spot, but not dollar spot; excellent for Florida.	¾-1"	Spring	5-10
Medium texture, dark green; makes early spring recovery; slow spreading.	¾-1"	Spring	5-10
Dark green, fine texture, disease resistant.	¾-1"	Spring	5-10
Dense, weed-free turf; tolerates heavy wear, used on many football fields.	¾-1"	Spring	5-10
Thick growth; adapted to sandy soils; year-round color.	2-2½"	Spring	4-5
Blue-green; excellent ornamental turf, but does not withstand heavy wear.	2-2½"	Spring	4-5
Coarse, relatively unattractive turf, but easy to maintain.	2"	Spring	4
Easily maintained, good for heavy soils; has unattractive brown winter color.	1-1½"	Spring	2
Best grass where water is unavailable; thrives when mowed low.	1-2"	Spring	Seldom required.
Bunch-type grass, not as desirable as buffalograss, but drought-resistant.	1-2"	Spring	Seldom required.
Withstands long, dry periods and heavy traffic if not mowed closely.	2"	Fall	Seldom required.

Who needs weeds?

The battle to keep your lawn free of weeds seems unending. The creepers sneak in among the grass stalks, the dandelions spread their leaves and pop their yellow heads. Sometimes it seems that if you take your eyes off the grass for 10 minutes, some weed sneaks in and establishes itself.

There are three ways to win this battle: Keep the weeds out in the first place; slaughter them in the spring, before they get moving; or fight them throughout the growing season.

The best way is the first way—and you keep weeds out by building a thick, healthy, vigorous stand of grass. Strong, thick grass crowds out the weeds, or smothers them before they can take hold. If you have a good thick lawn, don't mow it too close, because this allows the weeds to get in. And when you water, do it thoroughly be- cause light waterings, which don't soak into the soil, will water the weeds near the surface, but won't water the deeper grass roots.

The next best method of fighting weeds is to clobber them with a pre-emergent herbicide. Your dealer has a number of these, which you must apply early in the spring, before weed seeds have a chance to germinate. A good rule of thumb in many areas is to apply them before the lilacs bloom or the magnolia petals fall. By killing the weeds before they start, you can save yourself a lot of labor later.

Finally, there is the old method of day-by-day hand-to-hand combat. Today's herbicides are pretty good and take out some of the work, but this type of treatment is still a season-long nuisance. If you can identify the unwanted visitors in your yard, you can buy a herbicide specifically designed for them. If you have a fine collection

ESTABLISHING A LAWN

SEEDING IS THE EASIEST and least expensive way to establish a lawn. For even distribution of the seed, broadcast it with a mechanical spreader. Rake the area after seeding, then mulch lightly with straw.

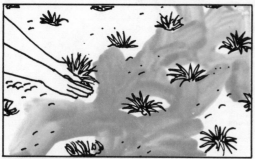

PLUGGING IS A GOOD WAY to start zoysia and similar grasses. The plugs are small squares or cylinders of sod and usually are set about 12 in. apart. Set them closer if you want more rapid coverage.

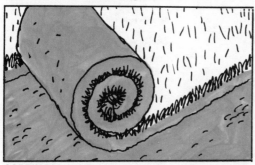

SODDING IS EXPENSIVE, but is the quickest way to an established lawn. Prepare the surface as you would for seeding, then roll it lightly. Dampen the soil then lay the sod over it. Butt the sod strips closely. Roll the completed lawn, then water regularly.

SPRIGGING IS INEXPENSIVE and an excellent way to start Bermuda and zoysia lawns. In this method you propagate individual runners which are broken from established sod. A neighbor with a good lawn may be willing to contribute the sprigs. If you want fast coverage, set the runners close together. Firm the soil over each sprig with your feet, and keep the sprigged area moist for several weeks or until the sprigs take hold and begin to spread. This is a good job for very hot weather because the sprigs spread very fast at this time, but you must keep them well watered or you will lose them.

of weeds, with nothing predominant (including the grass), get an all-purpose weed killer.

Herbicides come in liquid concentrate form, which you mix with water and spray on, and in dry form, which you apply with a spreader. You can buy pre-emergent weed killers mixed with fertilizer, so you can both weed and feed your lawn with one shot in the spring. This is probably the handiest way to get both jobs done.

Note that herbicides will kill any type of broad-leafed plant or flower. Be careful as you spread or spray the stuff not to let any of it drift into the flower beds. And reserve any sprayer used with weed killer for weed killing use in the future, because it is extremely difficult to get rid of all traces of herbicide. Get a second sprayer for spraying insecticides.

Crabgrass confrontations

Crabgrass is a tough adversary, but we finally have good ways to control it. To understand what you are up against, you have to know a little about crabgrass.

Throughout the summer and fall, the crabgrass in your lawn produces seeds. These seeds lie dormant until early spring, when they start sprouting. By midsummer, you can see the plants—coarse, broad eyesores, unwanted islands in an otherwise nice lawn. Each plant dies in the fall, but by then has left behind its own legacy of seeds. Unfortunately, we now know that crabgrass seeds can stay dormant for as long as 50 years.

Fortunately, pre-emergent crabgrass-killing herbicides do a great job of killing the seedlings just after they sprout. This means that with some smart action in the spring, you can stay free of crabgrass through the growing season. But you still must go on with the pre-emergence treatment the following spring, because older seeds may germinate. In time, perhaps after two or three years, you may get rid of most of the seeds. But don't count on it.

The weed-and-feed combinations mentioned earlier, if applied early enough, are good for both feeding the lawn and killing the crabgrass sprouts. Normally you'd give this treatment late in April. If you are putting in a new lawn, you can buy a mixture containing both fertilizer and crabgrass killer which can be applied the same day you sow the grass seed.

Finally, you'll find crabgrass killers on your dealer's shelf for use after the plants have started to grow. Good advice: get after crabgrass as soon as you can. It grows very fast in the late

FERTILIZER

FERTILIZER	FERTILIZER NEEDED TO SPREAD 1 POUND OF NITROGEN OVER 1000 SQ. FT. AREA
5-10-5	20 Pounds
4-12-4	25 Pounds
5-10-10	20 Pounds
10-10-10	10 Pounds
8-8-8	13 Pounds
10-6-4	10 Pounds
8-6-4	13 Pounds
4-8-4	25 Pounds
6-12-4	17 Pounds
Processed sewage sludge	17 Pounds
Ammonium nitrate	4 Pounds
Ammonium sulfate	5 Pounds
Nitrate of soda	7 Pounds
Steamed bonemeal	50 Pounds
Cottonseed meal	17 Pounds
Peanut hull meal	50 Pounds
Cocoa shell meal	50 Pounds
Dried cattle manure	50 Pounds
Dried sheep manure	70 Pounds
Sewage sludge	50 Pounds
Tobacco stems	50 Pounds
Urea	3 Pounds
Processed tankage	13 Pounds
Soybean meal	17 Pounds
Urea-form	3 Pounds

spring, and the bigger it gets, the harder it is to kill. Most crabgrass killers of this type require two applications, 7 to 10 days apart.

Watering know-how

How the lawn is watered is a lot more important than most homeowners realize. The reason is simple: Roots, including grass roots, always go where the water is. If you water frequently but only to a depth of an inch or two, then your grass roots will grow in that moist inch or two.

Good grass roots should go deep—six inches or more. When you water lightly, you not only keep them near the surface, but you also provide a soggy surface soil in which weeds thrive.

The right way to water your lawn is to soak it so that the soil is wet to a depth of at least six inches—and even deeper if possible. This means at least two hours of sprinkling with the average sprinkler, and perhaps more. (Test your sprinkler by placing some coffee cans around the yard while it sprinkles. Note how long it takes two inches of water to collect in each can. That's about how long the sprinkler should run to properly soak your lawn.)

After the lawn has been soaked, leave it alone for a week. Let it dry out, then soak it the same way. If there is rain between your soakings, take this into account. You can test the moisture of the ground by pushing a screwdriver into it. If it goes down easily to a depth of six inches, the ground is wet. The harder it is to push in the

screwdriver, the drier the soil.

Many sprinklers will cause the water to run into the street before it has had a chance to soak into the ground. They either apply the water too fast or the soil absorbs it slowly. If this is your problem—then divide your watering time. Run the sprinkler for half an hour, wait an hour, and run it again.

Keep in mind that all soils are different, so you must judge your own yard. Sandy soils take water fast, and clay soils absorb slowly. Spend a little time determining just how to get water into the top six inches of your lawn without wasting it. It will pay off in a healthier stand of grass.

Final watering hint: when you walk across your grass and leave footprints, water is needed. Grass which has enough moisture bounces back so your footprints don't show.

Mow your grass

It has been said that improper mowing has ruined more good lawns than any other single thing. Maybe so. It is certain that bad mowing can throw your grass into shock, even if it doesn't actually ruin the lawn.

There are three ways to give your lawn a bad time with a mower: First, cut it too short. Second, let it grow too long before cutting. And third, cut it with a dull blade, which tears rather than cuts.

The height of the cut depends, of course, on the type of grass. Bermuda, zoysia and bent grasses must be cut very short to keep the thatch from building up. But bluegrasses should be left fairly long—longer than most people believe. Two inches is a good minimum.

The reason is that the leaf of the bluegrass produces the food on which growth and root development depend. If you cut too much of the green blade, you cut down on the plant's ability to develop food. In addition, bluegrass likes a cool soil, and longer leaves shade the soil and help keep it cool. This is the main reason why it is good to allow bluegrass to grow even longer in very hot weather.

How often to cut? When the grass is about 1/3 taller than its regular height. This may mean frequent cutting during strong growth periods, but there is a good reason. When you allow the grass to grow too tall, then cut it short, you expose stems which have been shaded to sunburn, and cut away too much of the green leaf. The lawn takes on a scalded look and may take a long time to recover from the shock.

Dull, knicked mower blades flail and slash at

GOOD LAWNKEEPING

KEEPING THE EDGE NEAT can be a problem. One way to reduce tedious hand trimming is to install a mowing strip at least 6 in. wide around flower beds. You can use brick, small concrete blocks, and even railroad ties.

THE AREA AROUND A TREE can be hard to mow and usually is shaded so grass doesn't grow well. Remove the grass and cover the area with wood chips or pebbles. Another method is a good ground cover and edging.

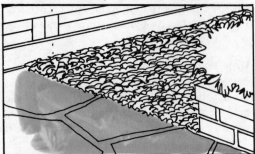

SMALL GRASSY AREAS are troublesome to mow and to keep neat looking. Best way is to remove the grass and install attractive landscaping additions such as raised flower beds or small walking areas of brick or patio stone.

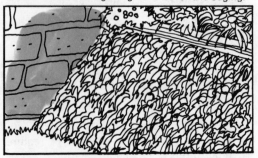

COVER STEEP SLOPES with ground cover. Slopes are difficult to mow and present watering and erosion problems. Use English ivy, which holds the soil well, or myrtle or pachysandra. Flower plantings won't help here.

the tender grass blades, ripping them instead of cutting. The result is frayed ends which turn brown, an additional shock to the plants. Use a file to sharpen the blade, disconnecting the mower's sparkplug before you begin. (You run a risk of starting the engine by turning the blade if you don't take this precaution.)

Additional mowing hints: Pick up the sticks and stones in the yard before you begin to mow. Don't try to cut wet grass, but wait until it has dried. Use a bag to collect clippings as you mow. Accumulated clippings can create a thick thatch which smothers the grass roots and which harbors insects and disease. And finally, always clean the mower blades when you finish.

How to rejuvenate your lawn

If your yard looks as if it were covered with a green shag rug, you still may be able to pump some life into it. If about half of the area is still covered with good perennial grasses, there is hope. Plan to begin the rejuvenation in the middle of August. Here are the steps to follow:

1. Apply weed killer according to the directions on the can to kill the broadleaf weeds. Read the herbicide labels to get the best one for your problem. If crabgrass is evident, be sure the label specifies that the herbicide kills crabgrass too.

2. If no lime has been applied for four years, apply dolomitic agricultural limestone at the rate of 50 to 75 lbs. per 1000 sq. ft.

3. Apply fertilizer. Use the fertilizer formula to be sure you apply 1 lb. of nitrogen per 1000 sq. ft.

4. Mow closely. Rake the bare areas to loosen the soil.

5. Seed perennial bluegrass/fescue mixture into the bare areas (in the north), or plant stolons of grasses (in the south). Use 1-2 lbs. of seed per 1000 sq. ft.

6. Water the seeded or planted areas lightly. Keep soil moist until seed germinates and seedlings are established.

7. Continue to mow whenever the older grass needs it.

8. Early in the spring, apply a pre-emergent crabgrass killer and give the lawn its first feeding. By June, you should see a considerable improvement, and by the end of the summer, a thick turf should have developed.

Fall lawn care for healthy summer grass

■ WHILE YOU'RE TRIMMING and getting your shrubs ready for winter, why not do the same for your lawn? Fall is the best time to revitalize it. The time is right for three things:

1. Seeding: Those warm days and cool nights provide the best growing conditions. As long as the days stay warm, there's time.

2. Fertilizing: Feeding the lawn with a slow-release fertilizer will help it stay green later and turn green sooner in the spring.

3. Controlling weeds: Now, while weeds are still growing, is the time to spread a weed control (if you're not seeding this fall), or a product that will fertilize *and* weed.

Seeding

Seeds need protective grooves in which to lodge, so slice the soil ¼ in. deep with a sharp-tined rake or a rented power rake.

Next, put down seed and fertilizer separately. Use of a spreader will assure even and economical results. Both can be put down the same day. Buy top quality seed—it will determine the kind of lawn you have for years. The fertilizer should be one specially made for new seeding.

If you seed on bare ground, lightly mix the seed into the soil with the back of a lawn rake. Light mulching with straw so you can still see the ground helps hold moisture.

Once the seed has germinated, keep the top inch of ground moist until the seedlings are established.

For an even healthier lawn feed it again after about six weeks with a slow-release type of fertilizer that's high in nitrogen—the first number of three listed on the bag.

FERTILIZER can make a difference. Right side was fertilized; other wasn't.

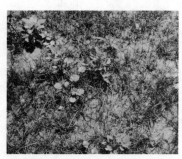

A NEWLY seeded area is patchy with weeds; many will die when mowed.

COMPARE untreated lawn and one treated with weed control and fertilizer.

CUTAWAY (left) shows dandelion with long tap-root before weed control treatment. Two weeks later dandelion (center) is failing; a month later (right) it's absorbed.

Fertilizing

Grass needs help to replenish itself after the hot, often dry summer. In the fall more than at any other time of year, grass plants will multiply themselves when fertilized, producing new leaves and new off-shoot plants (called rhizomes) to thicken and strengthen the lawn. Fall-fed grass plants also produce and store carbohydrates over the winter, which the plants use in the spring. This late fall feeding speeds green-up in spring.

Select a long-acting fertilizer that nourishes for six to eight weeks. You can cover a 5000-sq.-ft. lawn in an easy half-hour walk with a lawn spreader. Start by fertilizing a strip at each end of a lawn section. To prevent fertilizer oversatura-tion, shut off the spreader as you reach each strip and turn around.

Controlling broadleaf weeds

To be an instant expert on controlling dande-lions and other broadleaf weeds, you need to know two things:

● The control should be put on the weeds during their active growing season, since its effectiveness depends on being absorbed by the plant.

● The control particles need to stick to the leaves for at least 24 hours, so the leaves should be moist when the control is spread. Water the lawn before spreading on weed control or do it when the grass is moist from early morning dew.

FALL LAWN CARE TIPS

1. **When the weather cools** and your grass is slowing its growth, mow the lawn about ½ in. lower than its usual height. Letting it go into winter short cuts down on the possibility of its becoming diseased.

2. **Both your shrubs and lawn** need plenty of moisture to help them survive the winter. If nature doesn't cooperate, give your grass 1 to 1½ in. of water a week. You can tell how long you need to leave the sprinkler on by setting out three or four tin cans at varying distances from it. After a set period of time—say, a half hour—find the average of the water depths in the cans. If it's ¼-in., for example, one hour's sprinkling will give the lawn ½ in. of water.

3. **Rake up the fall leaves** and debris so they don't mat the grass. But it *is* wise to pile leaves around shrubs. It gives them added winter protection.

4. **Sprinkle a little fertilizer** on the compost pile between layers of grass clippings and garden debris. You'll get quicker, richer compost in the spring to use for your early garden.

5. **Don't bother trying** to rake up the late-season crabgrass. The frost will kill it permanently. Crabgrass comes up new each year from seed. You can stop it from cropping up next spring by putting down a crabgrass preventer, which you can buy combined with fertilizer. Even if you need to re-seed this fall, you can leave the dead crabgrass in the ground. The new grass will sprout up through it.

Collapsible leaf cart

■ BEAUTIFUL shade trees around your house are a blessing in the summer, but they present an almost unmanageable situation when fall comes. Here's one solution: a leaf cart with three collapsible sides that holds well over 100 bushels of dry leaves.

To make the cart, begin by assembling the joint for the rear uprights and the base supports. Position the top of the notch 36⅛ in. from the top of the upright. If you are using 6-in.-dia. wheels, bore the axle hole 1¾ in. from the bottom of the upright. If you use different wheels, allow clearance so when sides are dropped they won't hit wheels.

After the joint is complete, attach the crosspieces to the base supports and rear uprights, then install the hitch assembly as shown. Next, assemble the three folding sides and attach the hinges. The detail shows how to build sides and front so they meet compactly.

You'll have to experiment to position the hinges on the front base crosspieces. This was accomplished here by having the hinges overlap slightly. When folded up, the sides are splayed slightly because the upper rails (H) butt against the outside edge of the rear uprights.

Install the chicken wire with staples, using one continuous strip for the back, bottom and front, and one 8-ft. piece on each side. Nail the lattice over the wire for extra support; install 2-in. hooks and eyes on all four corners. Finally, bend 6d nails into small loops to act as clips that join the wire on the sides to that on the bottom.

MATERIALS LIST—LEAF CART

Key	No.	Size and description (use)
A	2	1½ × 1½ × 96″ fir (base rail)
B	2	1½ × 3½ × 42″ fir (rear upright)
C	1	¾ × 4½ × 36″ fir (crosspiece)
D	2	½ × 5 × 10″ plywood (gusset)
E	1	¾ × 2½ × 36″ fir (crosspiece)
F	4	¾ × 2½ × 36″ fir (side upright)
G	4	¾ × 2½ × 35¼″ fir (front corner upright)
H	2	¾ × 2½ × 96¾″ fir (side rail)
I	6	¼ × 1½ × 34″ lattice (cleat)
J	4	2″ hook and eye
K	4	¾ × 2½ × 32″ fir (base crosspiece)
L	8	2″ double-hole utility hinge
M	2	1½ × 1½ × 40″ fir (A-arm)
N	2	¾ × 1½ × 5″ fir (spacing block)
O	1	1½ × 3½ × 20″ fir (hitch tongue)
P	1	½ × 5″ carriage bolt, nut, washer (hitch pin)
Q	1	5⁄16 × 4″ carriage bolt, nut, washer
R	2	¼ × 3½″ carriage bolt, nut, washer
S	2	¼ × 2″ carriage bolt, nut, washer
T	2	¼ × 2¾″ carriage bolt, nut, washer
U	2	¼ × 4″ carriage bolt, nut, washer
V		36″-wide chicken wire, about 32′ long
W	2	6″-dia. wheels with nylon bushings
X	2	6½″ × dia. to suit, machine bolt, nut and spacing washers
Y	2	¼ × 4½″ carriage bolt, nut, washer
Z	10	2″ No. 8 fh wood screws

Misc.: 4d nails, ⅝″ U-shaped staples

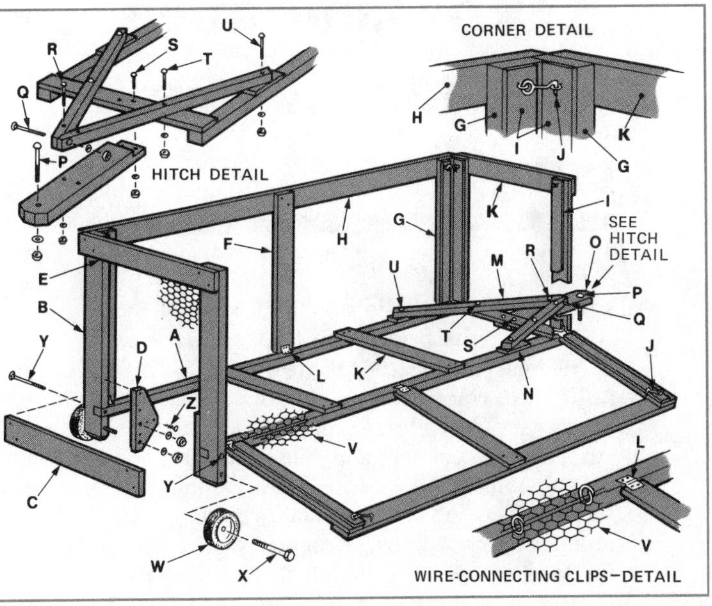

CORNER DETAIL

HITCH DETAIL

SEE HITCH DETAIL

WIRE-CONNECTING CLIPS—DETAIL

How and when to de-thatch your lawn

■ IS YOUR LAWN in trouble in spite of the good care you've been giving it? Does it seem to be thinning out instead of growing thick and lush? Have you been plagued with lawn insects or had severe outbreaks of diseases such as striped smut, leaf spot and dollar patch?

If you have been doing everything you should—weeding, feeding and watering—but nothing seems to bring your green carpet up to the level of your neighbors', there is a pretty good chance that your grass is choking to death.

There are two chief causes for this choking: a build-up of thatch deposits on the soil at the base of the grass plants; and dense, overcompacted soil. These two conditions prevent air, water and nutrients from getting to the grass roots, and as a result, the grass is slowly choking and starving.

Fortunately, both conditions can be cured and your lawn restored to its original healthy condition.

Thatch. Stick your fingers down into the grass and scratch around. If you have thatch build-up, you can feel it. Thatch is the accumulation of dead grass, old clippings, leaves and other undecomposed organic matter. Thatch accumulates over a period of time, and as it builds up, it forms an almost impenetrable matlike layer over the soil. Air, water and fertilizer can't get through it efficiently. Root development is discouraged and the grass leaves become thin and scraggly. Tough weeds, which can thrive in almost any condition, take this opportunity to overpower the weak grass.

The thatch makes an ideal breeding ground for lawn insects, and many types of fungal spores

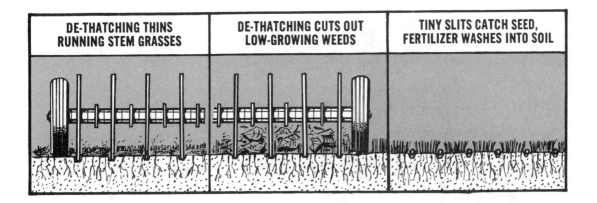

DE-THATCHING THINS RUNNING STEM GRASSES	DE-THATCHING CUTS OUT LOW-GROWING WEEDS	TINY SLITS CATCH SEED, FERTILIZER WASHES INTO SOIL

thrive in it. The total result, after the thatch has become well established, is weak, thin grass, rapid increase of weeds, diseased patches, and insect damage.

The major cause of thatch formation is grass clippings which you neglect to collect as you mow. If your lawn is in good balance, it can take a limited amount of clippings, which decompose on the ground and help in the formation of new soil. But if your soil is too acid, this decomposition may slow down, since composting requires an alkaline soil. In addition, some chemicals, notably pesticides, may reduce the rate of decomposition by destroying the microorganisms which carry out the composting process.

Soil compaction. Good soil is spongy. It breathes through a network of pores and capillaries. It accepts water readily and air can get through it. When good soil is severely compacted, its breathing network is crushed and shut off. Then more water runs off the surface than is absorbed into the soil, and little or no air gets in. Fertilizers applied to the surface never get to the grass roots.

The major cause of compaction is heavy traffic. Play areas and footpaths in the lawn usually are compacted. If you have observed such places, you know that they soon lose their grass covering, and new grass seed sown on the surface of such compacted places germinates, then quickly dies.

Earthworms, ants and other insects bore through the soil and play an important role in aerating it. They help to keep it loose and spongy. When you apply chemicals which kill them, you encourage compaction.

Compaction can take place all over the lawn

THE TYPICAL de-thatching rotor has 52 blades. These are individually removable so you can adjust the machine for light or medium combing. Ask your rental agent if adjustments are permitted.

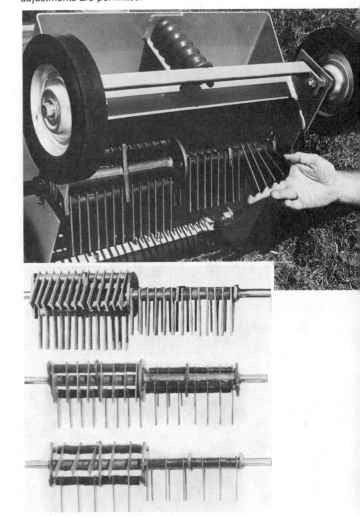

THIS VERTICAL-CUTTING mower cuts out dead plant matter with eight oil-tempered spring-steel blades.

YOU MAY FIND machines like this one, equipped with interchangeable reels. You can install the tine, the knife or the flail, depending on the type of problem.

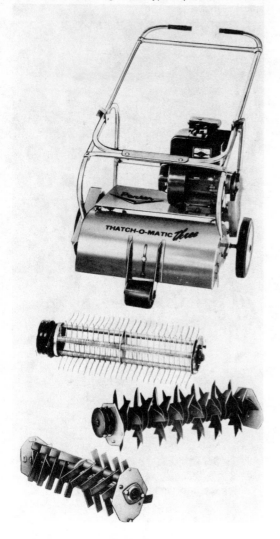

area. The soil may not become so dense as to kill the grass, but dense enough to cut the penetration of air and water by a half. The result is weak, sickly grass.

Compaction, too, can be cured. Best of all, you can cure it without digging up the lawn and starting over.

How can you tell when your lawn soil has become compacted? Make the screwdriver test. Try to insert the blade of a long screwdriver into the soil. If the soil is in good shape, you should be able to push the blade down into the soil about 4 in. without much trouble. If you really have to push, then the chances are your lawn needs aerating.

Pull the blade out of the ground carefully, pulling straight up, trying not to dislodge any of the soil deposits on it. Now look at the deposits. The lower part of the blade should have soil, but just above the soil, you may see a peat-like layer. This is thatch. If the layer of thatch is more than ½-in. thick, then you have a thatch problem as well as a compaction problem.

The solutions to both problems. You can rent de-thatching machines by the day to remove the thatch on your lawn. And you also can rent aerating machines which cut tiny plugs from the lawn surface and give the soil a chance to breathe once again.

De-thatching machines. Sometimes called a vertical mower, the average de-thatching machine is powered by a gasoline engine and is slightly larger than a rotary mower. Most de-thatchers have rotating reels designed to pull out the thatch and deposit it on the surface of the lawn—where you can collect it and haul it away.

There are three basic types of reels employed in de-thatching. Each type has a specific use:

Blade or flail type. This machine has a reel with 30 to 60 steel blades about ⅛ x 1 x 4 in. in size, either rigidly attached to the reel or free swinging. As the reel turns, the blades pass vertically through the living grass and cut into the thatch below, lifting it out. At the same time, the blades make narrow slits in the soil, providing some aeration and making a good bed for new grass seed.

The blade/flail type of de-thatcher is well-suited to bluegrass lawns. One version permits the removal of some of the blades to provide the best thinning and slicing action for lawns of southern bentgrass.

Tine type. The reel on this machine has 100 or so thin, wire-like flexible tines in place of flails and was designed specifically for use on blue-

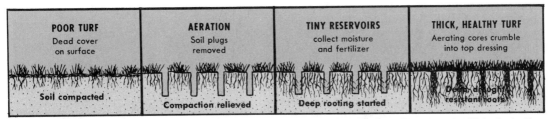

POOR TURF	AERATION	TINY RESERVOIRS	THICK, HEALTHY TURF
Dead cover on surface	Soil plugs removed	collect moisture and fertilizer	Aerating cores crumble into top dressing
Soil compacted	Compaction relieved	Deep rooting started	Deep drought resistant roots

THE ACTION which takes place in the soil after aeration is shown in these drawings. Plugs average 2½-in. in depth.

grass lawns. The tines provide a combing action and lift the thatch out with a minimal removal of living grass.

Knife type. This reel has from 25 to 50 tiny knives which remove some living grass as well as loose thatch. This unit is particularly effective on Bermuda, zoysia and centipede grasses commonly found in the southern sector of the United States. It helps in controlling the growth of such weeds as wild fescue, crabgrass and nimblewill.

You can expect to de-thatch about 5000 square feet of lawn an hour, and the average lawn will yield as much as 20 to 30 bushels of thatch per 1000 square feet. The best way to remove the thatch once the machine has deposited it on top of the grass is to rent a power sweeper for the purpose. You'll find hand raking pretty hard.

The thatch can be packed into plastic bags for disposal or you can use it in a compost heap. Mix in some black soil and some compost activator, which you can buy at the garden store, and later you will have a supply of black dirt for your lawn and garden.

Aeration machines. An aerating machine cuts small plugs, about 2½ in. deep, from the surface of the lawn, thus opening up pore spaces for penetration of air, water and fertilizer. Water getting into the holes helps the surrounding soil to expand and loosen up. Fertilizer goes straight to the grass roots and encourages good, quick growth.

One type of aerator has hollow tines which cut plugs on 5-in. centers. During operation, a plug of soil is forced into the central core of the tine.

Another type employs open, half-rounded spoons which scoop out a core of soil to give the surrounding earth room to expand. The action provides a loosening effect without disturbing the grass.

You can sweep the cores which are deposited on the grass to remove them, but experts recommend that you leave them where they fall. The action of rain will cause them to crumble and fall back to the surface as loose top soil.

You may find machines with solid tines or spikes instead of hollow tines or spoons. These poke holes in the earth's surface to permit water to enter the soil. They prevent runoff. But they also actually increase compaction as they punch their holes, and so should not be used on the average lawn with a compaction problem.

The best times for de-thatching and aerating are when the grass is growing vigorously—in the spring and fall. The fall is probably the best for aerating. Nature does her own aerating in the early spring through the action of alternate freezing and thawing of the surface soil.

Don't wait until too late in the fall to aerate. It is best to do it before mid-October. The reason is that the holes remain open for a while. If they don't fill, and the winter proves to be dry and lacking in snow, wind action can have a severe drying effect.

De-thatching is best in the spring, when the grass is growing most vigorously. The lawn has a month or so of good growing to recover from the shock of the treatment and reestablish itself before the slow-growing summer months.

How to prevent thatch buildup. The best way to prevent the buildup of thatch is to minimize the clippings you allow to stay on the lawn as you mow. Cut your grass often enough so that each clipping is short. If you allow the grass to grow too long, the long clippings are too much for the decomposing process and thatch begins to form. When the grass is long, use your grass catcher and collect the clippings as you go.

You can also prevent the build-up of thatch by vigorously hand raking the lawn every spring and fall. This is effective only when there is little buildup already present. Once the thatch has become established, the only effective way to deal with it is with a de-thatching machine.

Some experts recommend that de-thatching and aerating be done once a year—but not at the same time. The ideal annual program calls for de-thatching in the spring and aerating in the fall. However, most homeowners aren't eager to

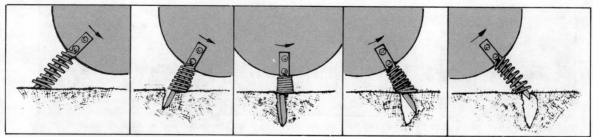

AS THE AERATING MACHINE rolls, its multiple spoons scoop out cores of soil, leaving holes every 5 inches or so.

incorporate this much work into their outdoor maintenance schedule and could work on a de-thatch-this-year-aerate-next-year schedule. This system will work best if care is taken to remove clippings during mowing.

Care after treatment. Following aeration or the removal of thatch, water the lawn thoroughly to stimulate recovery growth. If the lawn is in need of fertilizer, this is a good time to do it. Apply the fertilizer, then water the lawn to release the nutrients to the roots.

If the lawn has thinned out because of thatch or compaction, it may need reseeding. Both machines do an excellent job of preparing the lawn for seed, so this is a fine time to scatter new seed.

You'll have to be sure the soil is kept moist during the germination period. Spring and fall rains may do the job for you, but if they don't, you'll have to use the sprinkler.

The new seedling grass is shaded by the old grass, and so will thrive as long as there is sufficient moisture, but will shrivel quickly if the top ½-in. of soil dries out completely.

Special problems. Bermuda and zoysia grasses are slower to decompose than other types, and as a result, lawns consisting of them are more likely to have thatch problems. De-thatching these lawns at least once a year may be necessary.

If you have a sandy soil, very little aeration is necessary, and an aeration machine won't help. If your grass isn't healthy, you can assume that lack of air isn't the cause.

When installing a new lawn, starting with bare ground, you can do a lot to prevent compaction in later years. For one thing, mix plenty of sand into the top four to six inches as you prepare the ground for seed. This will help keep the topsoil loose.

For another, if the soil has a lot of clay in its composition, you can mix gypsum into it to prevent compacting. Take a sample of your soil to your garden store, or to your county agent. Talk to the county agent or someone at the store who knows soil, and work out a formula of materials you can add to condition the soil. These may include sand, gypsum, peat or lime, depending on the composition of the soil.

Garage door electric lock

TO OPEN the garage door, turn four knobs to the proper positions and press the button.

■ THIS COMBINATION LOCK for a garage door opener lets you activate the opener at the touch of a button without using easy-to-lose keys or magnets.

You can purchase the components at an electrical supply house (see parts list). You'll need a drill, screwdriver and soldering iron.

To make the opener work, you must complete an electrical circuit through four 12-position rotary switches and a momentary-contact pushbutton switch; then press the pushbutton switch that is normally open. You must know the correct position of all four rotary switches.

You can attach the device to the front of your garage or in another convenient spot. For additional safety, you might add a tamper switch that sounds an alarm if the box is removed.

To begin assembly, lay out the positions of the four holes for the rotary switches and the hole for the pushbutton on the cabinet. Allow a minimum 1¼-in. space between centers. Bore ⅛-in.-dia. pilot holes; bore ⅜-in.-dia. holes for the rotary switches and a ½-in.-dia. hole for the pushbutton. Feed the drill slowly to prevent grabbing or denting the aluminum face.

Install the rotary switches and pushbutton switch. Tighten the nut provided with each switch.

As a first step in wiring, solder a 2-in. piece of insulated wire to the center lug of the first rotary switch. Then solder this wire to any of the outside lugs of an adjacent rotary switch. Repeat this process for the second, third and fourth rotary switches. The fourth switch should be located next to the momentary-contact switch. With a 2-in. piece of wire, connect one of the outside lugs of the fourth rotary switch to a lug of the momentary-contact switch.

Strip two 2-in. pieces of insulated wire and solder the end of one piece to the remaining lug of the momentary-contact switch. Solder the remaining piece of insulated wire to one of the outside lugs of the first rotary contact. These short pieces of wire connect to the low-voltage wiring from your door operator.

Using bolt cutters, snip off the excess shaft supplied with the rotary switches. Install the knobs by sliding them over the shafts and tighten the mounting screws. Rotate all knobs so they point to the 12 o'clock position. Scratch or etch a mark on the faceplate above each knob. Then rotate each knob one click and repeat the process until the 12 positions have been marked.

Figuring the combination

To figure your combination, while facing the back of the panel, rotate each knob until the center wiper contact inside each switch is aligned with the terminal of the rotary switch that has been soldered to the wire. With all four switches aligned, note the position of each knob on the face of the panel. This is the combination of your lock.

By using any of the 12 positions on each rotary switch, any combination is possible. Prior to installing the combination lock, check continuity with an ohmmeter, if you can.

KNOBS rotate to a predetermined position.

WIRE the rotary and pushbutton switches. Use solderless connectors to connect to the door opener.

Carefully plan the installation position of the lock on the outside of your home or garage. Select a spot that provides some weather protection, or shelter it in a wooden box.

Mount the box securely to the garage by boring its back in three locations and securing it to the wall with sheet-metal screws. Next, bore a ⅜- or ½-in.-dia. hole through one side of the box and garage wall to permit the bell wire from the garage-door opener to be pulled into the box.

Remove electrical hazard

Note: To prevent accidental operation or electrical hazard while wiring, disconnect the power at the circuit breaker or unplug the garage-door opener from the connection to the house power supply.

Install the bell wire between the combination lock and the low-voltage contacts of the garage-door opener. Most have a two-screw terminal, so a doorbell button can be used from indoors to operate the door. Connect each wire to a screw on this terminal, tightening screws *securely*. Pull the other end of the bell wire into the combination-lock box, leaving 6 in. exposed. Connect the two short pigtails from the switches to the two ends of the wire, using solderless connectors. Test and install the faceplate.

Be sure to rotate all knobs after each use. This will prevent someone from gaining entrance by pushing the switch, or copying the combination for later use.

PARTS LIST—ELECTRIC LOCK

Amt. Description

Amt.	Description
4	templates numbered 1-12 (optional)
1	mini-utility box
4	12-position rotary switches
1	pushbutton switch
4	1" molded knobs for ¼" shaft 18-ga. insulated bell wire (length to suit)
1	door operator
2	solderless connectors
3	No. 8x1½" sheet-metal screws

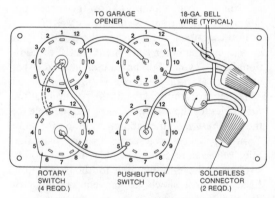

COMBINATION is now 5-11-11-9. Proposed change (dotted wire) would be 5-2-11-9.

Install a fast-set door lock

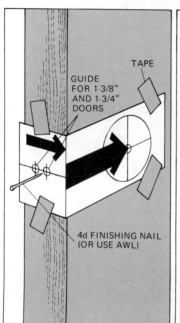

GUIDE FOR 1-3/8" AND 1-3/4" DOORS

TAPE

4d FINISHING NAIL (OR USE AWL)

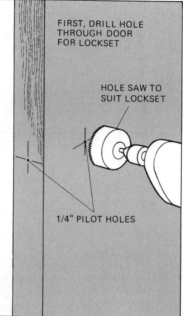

FIRST, DRILL HOLE THROUGH DOOR FOR LOCKSET

HOLE SAW TO SUIT LOCKSET

1/4" PILOT HOLES

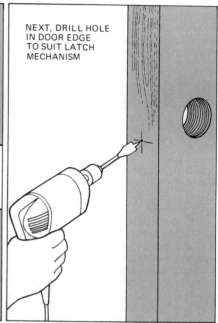

NEXT, DRILL HOLE IN DOOR EDGE TO SUIT LATCH MECHANISM

LOCATE THE HOLES FOR THE LOCKSET

The job starts by lining up the template (packed with the lockset or on inside of the box) with the door edge as in the drawing at left. Standard doorknob distance from floor is 36 to 38 in. Tape the template so it cannot shift, then drill ¼-in. pilot holes in door face and edge. Remove template and, using a hole saw to suit diameter of the lock you've bought, bore the large hole through door.

The best hole-saw technique is to drill halfway through from each side; while holding the drill at right angles—in both planes—to the door surface. Then, using a spade bit of a diameter to suit the latch mechanism, drill a hole in the edge for the latch.

To keep the door from moving while drilling, you simply wedge a pair of undercourse shingles under the door.

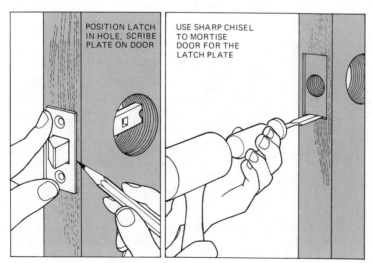

POSITION LATCH IN HOLE, SCRIBE PLATE ON DOOR

USE SHARP CHISEL TO MORTISE DOOR FOR THE LATCH PLATE

MORTISE FOR LATCH

Test-fit the latch mechanism in the hole you have just bored in the door edge; it should slide in and out freely without binding. Insert the latch in the door, firmly hold the plate against door edge and draw a pencil line around the plate. With a utility knife, score this pencil line. (This acts as a safety guide when mortising with a chisel.) Finally, using a ¾-in. chisel, remove the waste inside the mortise. *Caution:* When approaching the correct depth, avoid a too-deep mortise by stopping occasionally to check the mortise depth by inserting the latch.

INSTALL LATCH MECHANISM

Latch plate must be absolutely flush with the door edge: If it's too deep the door may not stay closed; if not deep enough the plate or screwheads may keep the door from closing. When plate is flush with the edge, permanently install it with screws provided.

Push plate fully into mortise and, with an awl, make pilot holes for the screws. Install the flathead screws, turning them fully home. If the latch plate has a sloped surface, the slope should be toward direction of door closing. For smooth lockset operation, bar extending into the door must be at right angle to door edge.

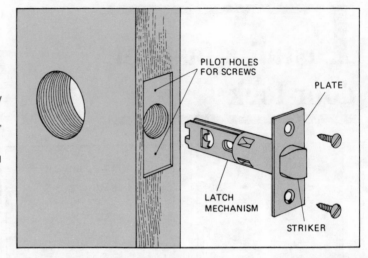

EXTERIOR TRIM GOES IN NEXT

Next, install the exterior trim (knob with the tie rods) through appropriate holes in the latch. Tie rods should slide freely, not bind against latch or door. Important: If installing a lockset with a key, place lock so the keyhole is at bottom of the knob (in 6:00 o'clock position). This is particularly important in installations where the lock is exposed to the weather. Correct installation allows moisture to escape, instead of trapping it and damaging the lockset. Never insert the key into the lockset before the installation is complete; you could disturb the tumblers.

FINISH LOCKSET INSTALLATION

Install interior mounting trim plate (rosette) over spindle and tie rods. On the lockset shown (there are several types of fast-set locks), the rosette is then rotated until holes in the rosette are centered over the tie rods. Hold both plates with one hand, insert lockset holding screws and catch the threads in the tie rods. Here, because the doorknob is usually partly in the way, it is best to use a slender-shank screwdriver to turn home the screws. Screws should be tightened until snug, not tightened with brute force, nor should they be so loose that the lock operates sloppily.

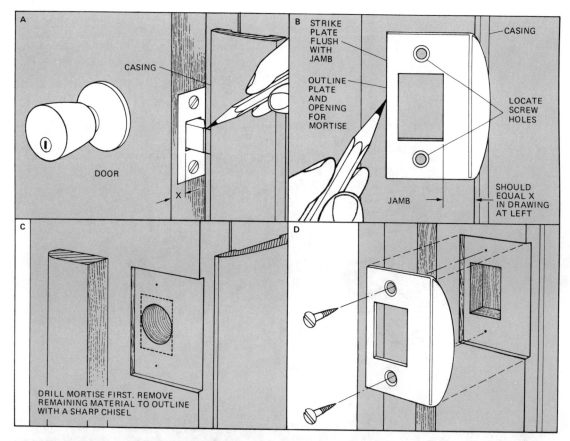

LOCATE STRIKER PLATE ON DOOR JAMB

To locate the exact position of the striker plate on the door jamb, close the door until the striker barely touches the jamb (drawing A above). Mark top and bottom of the striker on the jamb and open the door. Using a combination or try square, transfer these marks to face of the jamb—these are the horizontal marks that the opening in the striker plate must be located on.

Next, measure the distance from face of the door to the flat side of the striker in latch mechanism (dimension X in drawing A). The striker plate can then be precisely located as shown in drawing B. Horizontal edges of striker-plate opening are positioned on marks scribed on jamb earlier; vertical edge (of opening) nearest door is set back from edge of jamb to equal dimension X.

When satisfied that the striker-plate position is accurate, use a pencil to scribe lines for the plate mortise cut. Score the outline with a utility knife and chisel the mortise. After mortising the jamb so the striker-plate face is flush with the jamb, hold the plate in position in the

mortise and mark for the striker mortise (dotted rectangle in drawing C) and screw pilot holes. Using an appropriate-size spade bit (usually ¾ in. dia.), bore a hole in center of the mortise area (indicated by circle in drawing C). It is not necessary to drill completely through the jamb; just drill deep enough to fully accept striker. In most cases the bored hole will give satisfactory results, but for looks it is best to clean out this rectangle to the necessary depth using a chisel.

On many locksets, the edge of the striker plate toward the door is curved to such a degree that it will be necessary to remove additional material from the edge of the jamb near the door and, in some cases, the edge of the casing. You can do this with a chisel or pocketknife. Finally, position the plate and permanently install it using flathead screws provided. Open and close the door several times to check installation—be sure to stand on the hinge-pin side of the door in case the lock malfunctions.

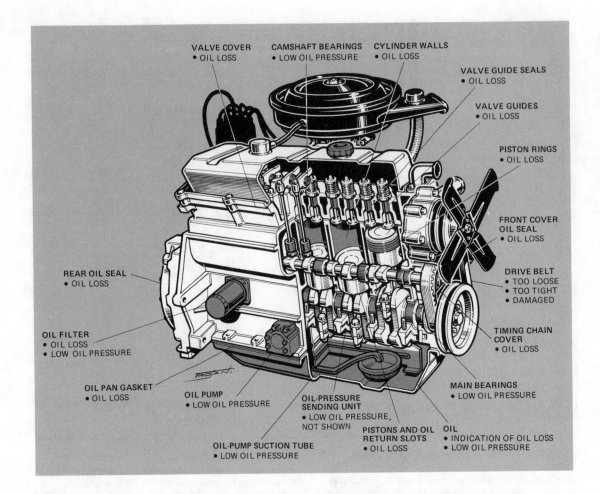

VALVE COVER
• OIL LOSS

CAMSHAFT BEARINGS
• LOW OIL PRESSURE

CYLINDER WALLS
• OIL LOSS

VALVE GUIDE SEALS
• OIL LOSS

VALVE GUIDES
• OIL LOSS

PISTON RINGS
• OIL LOSS

FRONT COVER
OIL SEAL
• OIL LOSS

DRIVE BELT
• TOO LOOSE
• TOO TIGHT
• DAMAGED

TIMING CHAIN
COVER
• OIL LOSS

MAIN BEARINGS
• LOW OIL PRESSURE

OIL
• INDICATION OF OIL LOSS
• LOW OIL PRESSURE

PISTONS AND OIL
RETURN SLOTS
• OIL LOSS

OIL-PRESSURE
SENDING UNIT
• LOW OIL PRESSURE,
NOT SHOWN

OIL-PUMP SUCTION TUBE
• LOW OIL PRESSURE

OIL PUMP
• LOW OIL PRESSURE

OIL PAN GASKET
• OIL LOSS

OIL FILTER
• OIL LOSS
• LOW OIL PRESSURE

REAR OIL SEAL
• OIL LOSS

Oil consumption troubleshooting

■ MANY CAR OWNERS are unsure what constitutes excessive oil consumption and what they can do about it. If your new car's engine uses oil in excess of the manufacturer's minimum, you have a warranty claim. If it doesn't, you don't have a claim.

As the years have passed, the manufacturer's "minimum" has shrunk. A while ago, using a quart of oil every 1500 miles was considered normal. Today, some manufacturers state that a new engine which uses a quart of oil every 700 miles is performing normally.

However, a certain number of new engines (and engines that have been overhauled) are oil consumers because of errors in production. An engine may get into the field with a defective front or rear oil seal, piston rings that have been improperly installed, or a defective oilpan gasket. After verifying the loss of a significant amount of oil because of a defective product, no reputable manufacturer or shop will refuse to take steps that will rectify the situation.

There is another reason for a new engine to demonstrate abnormal oil consumption. It has to do with the way some people "baby" a new car.

The cylinder walls in a new engine are smooth, and about 1000 miles of driving are needed before piston rings seat sufficiently to effectively prevent oil from seeping past.

However, if driving is too "cautious" during this period, piston rings may never seat. "Babying" the engine could cause glaze to build up between cylinder walls and rings, preventing effective sealing. If this happens, dismantling the engine, honing cylinder walls and replacing piston rings will be the only solution.

When breaking in a new car, you should follow the instructions laid down in the owner's manual.

If your driving is confined to the city, drive your new car on the expressway at least 10 miles at the speed limit. Doing otherwise will make the engine a candidate for oil loss.

Older engines, obviously, can become oil consumers because of wear. Any one of a number of defects will result in loss, including worn valve guides, damaged valve guide seals, worn piston rings, scored cylinder walls, worn piston-ring

grooves, worn pistons and clogged oil-return slots that prevent oil from returning to the oil pan.

However, things other than an internal engine problem cause oil loss in both new and old engines, and it pays for you to make careful checks before deciding to tear the engine apart.

Troubleshooting the problem

Here is how to proceed:

1. Start with the oil itself. Are you using oil designated by the car's manufacturer? Is the amount of oil in the engine to capacity? Does the car possess the right dipstick?

The dipstick is often overlooked in troubleshooting new cars. Occasionally, the wrong dipstick is put into an engine. To be sure this has not happened in your case, hold the dipstick next to one from the same model car, and make sure marks and length are the same.

TYPICAL ENGINE lubrication system. Cause of low oil pressure can be anywhere along the line.

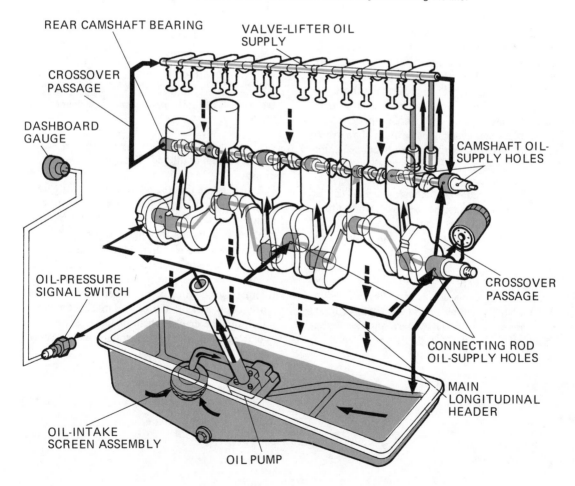

REAR CAMSHAFT BEARING

VALVE-LIFTER OIL SUPPLY

CROSSOVER PASSAGE

DASHBOARD GAUGE

CAMSHAFT OIL-SUPPLY HOLES

OIL-PRESSURE SIGNAL SWITCH

CROSSOVER PASSAGE

CONNECTING ROD OIL-SUPPLY HOLES

MAIN LONGITUDINAL HEADER

OIL-INTAKE SCREEN ASSEMBLY

OIL PUMP

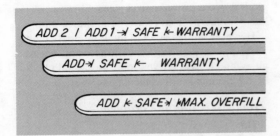

MANUFACTURERS make many different dipsticks; make sure you have the right one.

2. Spread clean paper on the floor beneath the engine and transmission. Keep the engine at a speed equal to 20–25 mph (1000–1200 rpm), and continue running it for several minutes after it has reached normal operating temperature.

After the engine has warmed up, momentarily race it at wide-open throttle and let it come back to fast idle. Do this about five times.

Shut off the engine and examine the paper. Look for oil. Also check the underside of the engine for fresh oil.

If a leak is uncovered, find where it is coming from and fix it. Primary places include the oil filter connection, oil pan, front and rear oil seals, valve covers and the timing-chain cover.

3. As the car is being accelerated, check exhaust smoke. Excessive oil burning is often indicated by gray or blue-gray smoke—not black or white. Black smoke signifies burning of an overly rich fuel mixture—white smoke is condensation being expelled.

4. Replace the PCV valve which, if clogged or defective, can cause oil to be drawn into the air cleaner housing. Examine the carburetor air filter element. Oil on this is the tipoff.

5. Check sparkplug tips for oil, which indicates oil loss.

Check low oil pressure

Oil pressure that is consistently low or pressure that takes a long time to reach acceptable limits after an engine is started are problems that shouldn't be slough¹ ed off. But neither should you panic over them.

Low oil pressure, especially when accompanied by a loss of oil, could mean that main or camshaft bearings are in poor shape. The engine may need overhaul. However, low oil pressure also has several other causes, which are less troublesome to eliminate. These are the ones to tackle first.

Important: Do not run the engine if low oil pressure is indicated. You could force the engine to freeze if a low oil pressure condition does in fact exist.

To get at the cause of low oil pressure, proceed as follows:

1. Check the engine oil level. Is it low?

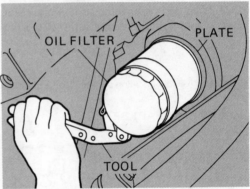

USE OIL-FILTER tool only for loosening a tight filter. Install filter hand tight only.

2. Is oil thin or diluted? Change the oil—check pressure.

3. Make sure that the oil pressure sending unit itself is in good shape. Replacing the unit on a hunch costs a dollar or two. That's a lot less expensive than tearing the engine apart.

4. Replace the oil filter. Maybe it is clogged.

5. You have to go inside now. Start at the oil pump. Check the pump pressure. Parts of the pump may be worn or the relief valve may be stuck. Also look at the oil-pump suction tube, which may be cracked, bent or loose.

6. Next stop is internal engine work. Sorry about that.

Lubricate your car

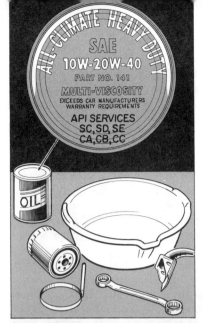

EQUIPMENT you need for changing oil and filter. Get the right oil.

■ AS ONE AUTOMOBILE model year has followed another, new cars have needed less servicing than their predecessors. Remember the 2000-mile motor-oil change recommended for, among others, the 1955 Ford? Now, many models go 10,000 or six months between oil changes, whichever interval comes first.

Sparkplugs are another example. Until 1975, it was normal to replace plugs every 10,000 or 12,000 miles. Since then, the catalytic converter, unleaded gasoline and the electronic ignition system have lengthened intervals between engine tune-ups and sparkplug changes. In a new General Motors car, you can drive 22,500 miles before new sparkplugs are called for.

However, despite these and other advances, car care remains an important part of owning a new, as well as an older, model. Failure to maintain a car leads to

■ Recurring mechanical headaches.
■ Increased cost of fuel and repairs.
■ Reduced vehicle life.

More often isn't too often

Those who are conscientious about caring for their cars often ask: "In maintaining a vehicle, should I follow the interval recommendations suggested by the manufacturer, or should I perform services more frequently?"

The more frequently you do certain services, the greater your chance of averting trouble. This does not mean you have to replace sparkplugs, air-cleaner filter, drive belts, shock absorbers and other parts before they have outlived their usefulness. A part should be replaced on an as-needed basis when an operational problem or an inspection tells you it is no longer performing properly.

There are other services that you should do on a mileage or time-period basis. These include oil and oil-filter changes, other fluid changes (automatic transmission, for example) and lubrication. They contribute to longer car life if done more frequently than the manufacturer recommends.

Engine lubrication and fluid-level inspection

The engine and some associated parts (brakes, radiator, transmission, for example) are fluid reservoirs. Fluids are a car's lifeblood. Without them, the car will not run or should not be run. This section discusses motor oil and how to change it; then, how to check some important fluid levels.

Oil lubricates engine components, reducing friction between moving parts and minimizing wear. Oil also cleans the engine, helps cool it, protects it against rust, and seals the cylinders. Most engines, depending on size, take a maximum of four to six quarts of oil.

Oil is stored in the oil sump (also called oil-pan or crankcase), which is a storage pan attached to the bottom of the engine. An oil pump siphons the oil through a pickup and filtering screen in the sump, and pumps it into the oil filter.

The oil filter does the job of removing dirt particles held in suspension by oil. Eventually, the filter becomes loaded with contaminating matter. Thus, it has to be replaced.

Manufacturers insist that an oil filter need not be replaced every time oil is replaced. "Every other oil change is sufficient," they contend.

However, there are some who don't see the logic of contaminating four to five quarts of fresh oil with the one quart of dirty oil remaining in the oil filter.

Pressure forces the oil from the oil filter into the engine and through galleries and passages to main bearings, connecting-rod bearings, camshaft bearings, rocker arms and other parts. In the process, the oil picks up and retains particles, and the oil additives and detergents begin wearing out. To avert engine damage that may be caused by a buildup of sludge formed by dirt-laden oil, oil should be changed before a critical point is reached.

Manufacturer-recommended oil-change intervals reflect this critical point. If the car is driven under "severe" conditions, manufacturers suggest cutting the recommended interval in half. Severe conditions include using the car mainly for stop-and-go driving, pulling a trailer or driving in desert areas.

Owners manuals provide manufacturer-suggested intervals. They also give the viscosity and type oil the manufacturer feels is best for your individual driving conditions. However, additional information regarding oil may be useful.

What viscosity numbers mean

Numbers you find on cans of oil—such as SAE 10W-50, SAE 30—are viscosity (or weight) numbers, which indicate the thickness of the oil. The higher the number, the thicker the oil.

SAE stands for Society of Automotive Engineers, which established the grading system, and W means the oil is intended for use in cold weather. The W designation is particularly important to keep in mind when temperatures drop to 32° F. or below. Above that level, oil having a viscosity number without W works satisfactorily.

When you start an engine in cold weather, oil with a low viscosity number (for example, SAE-10W, SAE 5W-30, SAE 20W-40) flows readily, reducing friction that might otherwise make starting difficult. Oils with high viscosity numbers (SAE 30 or 40) become thick in cold weather and usually make it harder to start your engine.

However, there is a drawback to using oil with a low viscosity number. As the engine gets hot, oil gets thinner. An oil with low viscosity to begin with may not give the engine the protection it needs.

Since more than one grade of oil is usuable over any one temperature range, you have to decide which is best.

One of the most important points to consider in selecting the right viscosity of oil for your car is the type of driving you do. For instance, 10W oil may be ideal if you live in a cold part of the country and drive under ideal conditions. But if you make long trips and carry heavy loads in the car, you will need the cold-starting advantages of a 10W oil plus a higher viscosity oil to protect engine parts. You would, therefore, select a 10W-30, 10W-40, or 10W-50 oil.

Another factor to think about in choosing oil is whether to buy a multigrade or single-grade product. Single-grade oil is less expensive, but there are other considerations.

Multigrade vs. single-grade oil

Multigrade oils are those that have two numbers, such as SAE 5W-30, SAE 10W-30, SAE 20W-50. Multigrade oil allows engine starting in cold weather while providing the protection of high-viscosity oil when the engine is hot. Its biggest advantage is that you don't have to change oil as the seasons change.

Multigrade oils contain special additives called polymers. As engine heat rises, the polymers change the character of the oil to prevent oil from thinning too much. Such oils are convenient, too, but no multigrade has quite as much high-temperature viscosity as the corresponding single grade. For instance, 10W-40 oil isn't as thick in a hot engine as a single-grade 40.

You get a little better protection at high temperatures with a single-grade oil. To take advantage of this protection, the oil generally has to be changed from one grade to another as the seasons change. An exception to this involves use of SAE 20W-20 oil.

Incidentally, if your car is burning oil, you can cut consumption until you are able to repair the engine by using a high viscosity single-grade oil.

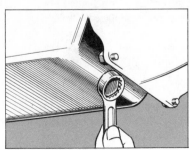

WITH ENGINE warm, remove the oilpan plug and let the old oil drain out.

REMOVE OIL FILTER. It should come off easily; if not, refer to text.

BEFORE installing new filter, spread oil over gasket to help seal filter.

What API letters mean

The American Petroleum Institute (API) tests motor oil for its ability to prevent wear, rust, corrosion, sludge and contamination. The oil is then classified. Letters designating the API recommended oil for your car should appear on the can of oil you buy. Classifications (see below) should be observed in selecting the right oil for an engine, since the right oil helps prolong engine life.

API OIL CLASSIFICATION SYSTEM

Letter Designation	Description	For Use in (model year)
SA	Straight mineral oil.	Not recommended.
SB	Straight mineral oil with anti-oxidant and antiscuff properties.	Not recommended.
SC	Meets automobile manufacturers' warranty requirements.	1967 and prior years.
SD	Meets automobile manufacturers' warranty requirements.	1970 and prior years.
SE	Meets automobile manufacturers' warranty requirements.	1980 and prior years.

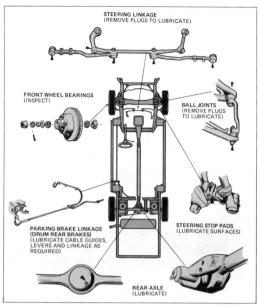

THIS IS a typical lubrication guide that you will find in service manuals.

How to change oil and filter

Note: Do this after the engine has been run and is warm. The engine should be turned off.

1. Place a waste pan under the crankcase drain plug. The car wheels may remain on the floor or the front may be raised. Engage the parking brake, place the automatic transmission in PARK or the manual transmission in gear, and place chocks around the rear wheels to keep the car from moving.

2. Loosen the crankcase drain plug. You can probably use an adjustable open-end or box wrench. Then, unscrew the plug by hand.

If the drain plug is countersunk, get a special drain-plug wrench of the correct size. Trying to loosen the plug with a conventional wrench may ruin the plug or damage the oilpan.

3. Wait for the crankcase to empty. This usually takes about three minutes, but don't be hasty. The more dirty oil you allow to drain, the less dirty oil remains in the engine.

4. Screw the drain plug carefully back into the oilpan and tighten it by hand. Then, with a torque wrench, tighten the plug to 20 foot-pounds. If you don't have a torque wrench, tighten the plug snugly with the conventional (special) wrench, but do not overtighten it since you may distort the oilpan.

5. Place a waste pan under the oil filter, and use an oil-filter wrench to turn the filter counterclockwise. If the filter is frozen in place, hammer a chisel through the filter canister and smack the

chisel handle with a mallet. This will loosen the filter. Remove and discard the oil filter.

6. Clean the filter seating surface on the engine. Make sure none of the old gasket material stays stuck to the surface. Use a putty knife to scrape off gasket material.

7. Spread some clean engine oil on the gasket of the new filter and on the filter seating surface. This helps seal the filter to the surface.

8. Hand-tighten the filter, being careful not to cross or strip threads. Tighten the filter until the gasket just touches the seating surface. Then, hand-tighten the filter an additional one-half to three-quarter turn. Do not use a wrench; it may distort the filter.

9. Fill the crankcase through the oil filler to the capacity called for in the owner's or service manual. Check the dip-stick oil level to see that oil is at the full mark.

10. Start the engine and run it at fast idle for a minute or two. Turn off the engine and check for leaks at the crankcase drain plug and oil filter. If there is a leak, tighten the plug or filter a bit more. If the leak persists, the component is damaged.

Fluid level inspection

Inspect fluid levels after changing oil. The following outlines how to check the brake master cylinder, automatic transmission and cooling system, but don't forget the battery, differential, power-steering reservoir and other fluid components your car may have.

Brake master cylinder. Release the clip or bolt holding the master cylinder cover, and lift off the cover. The brake fluid level should be ¼- to ½-inch below the top of the cylinder.

If fluid is needed, draw it from a fresh container of the type of brake fluid specified by the manufacturer. Do not use brake fluid that has been stored in a can which has been opened. Fluid may be contaminated. Be careful not to get dirt in the master cylinder.

Automatic transmission. Each manufacturer recommends a somewhat different procedure:

1. American Motors. Warm up engine and transmission (10-mile drive or longer); idle the engine; place the transmission selector in NEUTRAL; check the level.

2. Chrysler. Warm up engine and transmission (10-mile drive or longer); idle the engine; move shift lever slowly through each gear position; pausing at each until the gear engages; move the shift lever back to NEUTRAL; check the level.

3. Ford. Warm up engine and transmission (10-mile drive or longer); idle the engine; move shift lever slowly through each gear position, pausing at each until the gear engages; move the shift lever back to PARK; check the level.

4. General Motors. The engine and transmission may be cold, warm or hot (see below); idle the engine; place the shift lever in PARK; check the level.

For all makes of cars, withdraw the dipstick and wipe it with a clean rag. (If you can't locate the dipstick, consult the owner or service manual.) Reinsert the stick, seat it fully, withdraw again and read the level. In all cases except GM, the level should fall between the FULL and ADD marks. Do *not* add fluid unless the level is below the ADD mark.

With a GM car, touch the fluid with clean fingers. If fluid is cool, the level should be ⅛- to ⅜-inch below the ADD mark; if fluid is warm, the level should be close to the ADD mark; if the fluid is hot (uncomfortable to the touch), the level should fall between the ADD and FULL marks.

To add fluid in all cases, insert a clean funnel in the dipstick tube and pour in the type of fluid recommended by the manufacturer in the owner or service manual. Automatic transmission fluid that is suitable for one car may not be suitable for another.

Do not allow fluid level to go above the FULL mark. Excessive fluid in the transmission may create an aerating condition, causing gear slippage.

Cooling system. Most new cars have coolant recovery systems. Coolant level is checked by looking through the clear-plastic coolant recovery tank. Many tanks have two level marks—COLD and HOT. If the level is below the mark for the engine temperature when you check the coolant, add coolant to the coolant recovery tank.

If an engine is not equipped with a coolant recovery system, check the coolant level by removing the radiator cap when the engine is cold. The coolant should be 1½ to 3 inches below the top of the filler neck.

Chassis and body lubrication

Refer to the lubrication chart for your car, which you may find in the service manual. If you cannot find it you can do without it by checking pivot points for grease fittings and using the list below for greasing other parts.

How to lube chassis ball joints

1. Grease fittings (often called zerk fittings) allow you to attach a grease gun to pump grease into ball joints, which are load-carrying, and into swivel points on a car's chassis. Some ball joints have been made with rubber plugs instead of grease fittings. These plugs should be removed, discarded and replaced with fittings.

2. Wipe the grease fitting clean; otherwise, you may pump dirt into a suspension or steering ball joint. Dirt increases wear and causes premature failure.

3. Attach a hand grease gun filled with chassis grease to the fitting.

4. If you are lubricating a Chrysler or General Motors car, pump the handle of the grease gun slowly until grease oozes from the bleed hole in the base of the ball joint seal or until the seal swells.

5. If you are lubricating an American Motors or Ford car, pump the handle of the grease gun slowly until the ball-joint boot starts to swell. You can see or feel the swelling.

6. If grease oozes out more than slightly between the tip of the grease gun and zerk fitting, replace the fitting, which is probably clogged.

Greasing other parts

There are many parts of a car that should receive grease to prevent squeaking, corrosion and premature wear.

WITH TOP RIM removed and discarded, the keg is sawed on a line 7 in. up from the bottom to cut away the staves on each side. Two full staves remain.

A CIRCULAR SHELF, 11 in. in diameter, is next nailed between the two upright staves that are left after cutting the keg. This is placed 4 in. from top.

PAINTED GREEN or tan with a dry brush so the wood shows through here and there, the keg takes on a worn antique look which adds to its rustic charm.

Magazine bucket

■ THERE'S HARDLY A THING that can't be put to new use once it's tossed out, and that goes for nail kegs. By retaining their rustic look and cutting away part of their sides, you can come up with real conversation pieces in the form of magazine buckets, knitting holders, smoking stands—you name it.

Chances are your hardware store will give you an empty. Remove the top band and select the two best staves opposite each other to support a circular shelf and a dowel handle. Draw a line 7 in. up from the bottom and saw off the other staves.

As a sewing basket, the keg can be fitted with a lift-out lid resting on three small blocks glued to the inside. A spool serves as a knob.

Finally, the keg is sanded a bit, inside and out, and given a painted, dry-brush treatment that leaves the wood bare in spots. Two coats of varnish complete it. This charming homespun item will be right at home with hooked rugs and spinning wheels.

A DOWEL HANDLE is added last. Place it between the staves at the very top. A nail in each end holds it. Lift-out lid can be added to the bucket bottom.

Tree for magazines and newspapers

■ HERE'S SOMETHING DIFFERENT in a newspaper and magazine holder. Standing 26½ in. high it will hold up to seven rolled magazines and papers.

The post is a piece 2⅞ in. sq. which is cross-bored on adjacent faces with a 2-in. power bit and fitted with a half-lapped "hall tree" base at the bottom and a lathe-turned finial at the top. If you don't have a lathe, you can forget the finial and simply point the end of the member like a fence post.

BYPASSING HOLES through the post are made with a 2-in. multi-spur bit chucked in the drill press.

When boring the holes, clamp a scrap board to the underside of the work so you'll have clean-cut holes when the bit emerges. The boring should be done on a drill press. The cross base is fastened to the end of the post with 2-in. flat-head wood screws and glue.

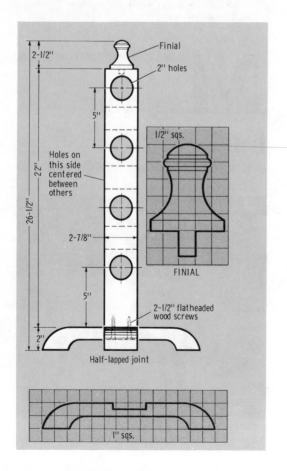

Finial

2-1/2"

2" holes

5"

1/2" sqs.

Holes on this side centered between others

2-7/8"

FINIAL

22"

26-1/2"

5"

2-1/2" flatheaded wood screws

2"

Half-lapped joint

1" sqs.

SIGHTING-IN SET-UP can be a simple card table, folding chair, a glove, rolled sleeping bag or a sandbag for barrel cushion and binoculars as spotting scope.

Zeroing-in a rifle

■ NO MARKSMAN, no matter how skillful, can hit anything consistently unless his gun shoots where he's aiming. The guarantee for a bull's-eye every time is top-grade equipment that is properly zeroed-in. This means gun sights that are adjusted correctly so you hit the target at which you're aiming. We all do miss at times, but the miss should be *your* fault—not the gun's.

The purpose of sights on rifles and handguns is well known to most shooters, but many do not realize it is possible and important to zero-in shotguns as well.

Most rifles have open sights

Almost all rifles come with simple factory-installed sights, known commonly as "open sights." The adjustable rear sight consists of a piece of metal with a V or U-shaped notch cut in the middle of the upper edge. The front sight usually is a fixed blade or bead that is lined up in the rear sight notch. The process of placing the front sight on the target and simultaneously lining it up with the rear sight is called the "sight picture." Obtaining the correct sight picture and repeating it without variation for every shot is the key element of accurate shooting.

Two other types of sights are also used on rifles. One is the rear aperture or "peep" sight with a circular disc and a small hole in the middle. The shooter looks though the hole and places the top of the front sight blade or post in the middle of the circle. The third type is the telescopic sight which magnifies the target and utilizes adjustable cross hairs, a single post, or a combination of both.

Theoretically, a perfectly sighted-in rifle, fired with a completely steady hold and a perfect sight picture, should put every bullet in exactly the same place. Actually, this doesn't quite happen, although it's possible to come very close. The limitations on perfect accuracy are the result of four variables. These include the limitations of your own eyesight in correctly lining up the sights on the target; the fineness of sight adjustments; the steadiness of your hold; and the inherent accuracy (or lack of it) of the rifle itself and the ammunition. All four limitations can be overcome somewhat. Peep and telescopic sights reduce eyesight limitations and permit finer adjustments. A steady rest helps. Highly sophisticated target rifles and custom ammunition are more accurate than standard rifles. But for normal hunting or plinking, any sporter rifle and standard ammunition made by reputable manufacturers have all the accuracy you will need.

You'll need a steady rest

Regardless of the type of rifle or sights you use, a steady rest is a must for zeroing-in. This should go under the fore-end of the rifle. Commercial rests can be purchased and are often available at club or public rifle ranges, but it's just as easy to improvise a rest out of an old pillow, a rolled up sleeping bag or several sand

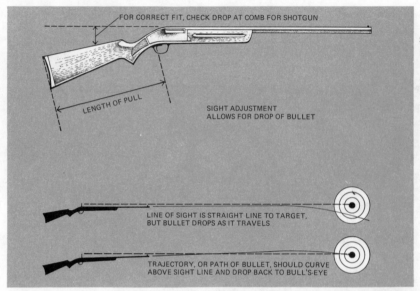

FOR CORRECT FIT, CHECK DROP AT COMB FOR SHOTGUN

LENGTH OF PULL

SIGHT ADJUSTMENT
ALLOWS FOR DROP OF BULLET

LINE OF SIGHT IS STRAIGHT LINE TO TARGET,
BUT BULLET DROPS AS IT TRAVELS

TRAJECTORY, OR PATH OF BULLET, SHOULD CURVE
ABOVE SIGHT LINE AND DROP BACK TO BULL'S-EYE

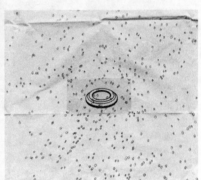

SHOTGUN IS POINTED rather than sighted. Proper fit helps determine accuracy and measurements shown at left can be adjusted or altered by a gunsmith.

GROUPING FOR SHOTGUN (above) shows the pattern clustered properly around a clay pigeon picture. Rifle two-shot groups (far left) are moved toward the center by moving rear sight in the same direction. Experienced handgunner can fire five-shot groups offhand for zeroing-in.

bags. The rest you choose should have flexibility to simulate the normal "give" of your hand when shooting without a rest. If you use a hard rest, place a sponge or thick glove between it and the rifle. Otherwise, the muzzle jump at firing will bounce the rifle upward off the hard surface and give you a shot that is high, and when you correct for it, the rifle will shoot low when the rest is no longer used.

The steadiest positions are prone (down on your stomach) or sitting at a bench or table. If there is a rifle range nearby, use it by all means. It usually offers fixed target holders, measured distances and shooting tables and positions. Otherwise, find a safe open area with a good backstop and pace off the desired range. Shoot from a prone position or use a folding chair and card table.

For .22-cal. plinking rifles, sight-in at 25 or 50 yards. Most hunting rifles in .22 cal. or the larger centerfire calibers are best zeroed-in at 100 yards.

Sighting-in your rifle

Here's the procedure for sighting-in. Set up your target and fire two shots as carefully as possible. Squeeze slowly and avoid jerking the trigger. If the two shots are on the paper and within a few inches of each other, mark the point midway between them and adjust the sights to move this point toward the bull's-eye. You always move the rear sight in the direction you want the bullet to go. If the group is low and to the left, for example, move that rear sight higher and to the right. If your first two shots don't even hit the paper, move your rest closer to the target until they do. Work the group in toward the bull's-eye, then return to your 50 or 100-yard position and make your final adjustments.

Final groups should be three shots and the zero should be in the middle of the triangle formed by the three holes. Many shooters wonder how small these final groups should be. This depends on you and your equipment. Generally, at 100 yards using open sights, you can expect three to four inches between the two most widely separated shots. Peep sights should reduce this to two to three inches, and telescopic sights could narrow it down to two inches or less. At 100 yards, top marksmen can cover five-shot groups with a nickel. For zeroing-in at 50 yards, divide the above figures by two; and at 25 yards, by four.

If you can't achieve groups as small as those mentioned, you may not have a steady enough rest, you may be jerking the trigger, your sights may be loose (check all mounting screws) or, sadly, you may just have a rifle of poor accuracy.

Shooters who sight-in rifles or switch sights frequently should consider purchasing a collimator. This device is hung on the end of the rifle barrel and permits preliminary sight adjustments before firing that should get your initial shots on the paper. And if you become a frequent rifle range shooter, a spotting or target scope lets you see where your bullets are striking without your leaving the shooting position.

Bullets, of course, are subject to the law of gravity and start dropping the instant they leave the rifle muzzle. Your line of sight will be a straight line to the target, but the bullet must follow a curve above the line of sight. As a result, a rifle sighted "dead on" at 100 yards will shoot a bit high at 50 yards and low at 150 and beyond because of bullet drop. Major ammunition manufacturers include trajectory charts in their ammo catalogs so you can determine where a bullet will strike at other than zeroing-in range and enable you to zero-in your rifle for, say, 200 yards while shooting at a 100-yard target.

Handguns

In general, handguns are less accurate than rifles and are shot at much shorter ranges. Proficiency is more difficult, and a beginner should try to get expert instruction. Some handguns without adjustable sights are acceptable for short-range plinking, but rear sight adjustment is needed for serious marksmanship.

Most experienced handgunners will zero-in their sights by shooting in their normal offhand position. Less practiced handgunners tend to spray their shots too widely for a useful group and need to use a rest. Sitting is one of the most convenient positions and should let you extend the gun at almost full arm's length so the sights will look the same as when you're shooting offhand.

Sit facing directly toward the target, draw your knees up about halfway to your chest, take a two-hand hold on the gun with the nontrigger hand underneath the butt, and rest your elbows on the inside of each knee. Fire five-shot groups, using the center as your zero point. Then adjust your rear sights as you would for a rifle, moving them in the same direction you want the bullet to move.

Shotguns

Your shotgun doesn't have sights in the normal sense and is pointed rather than aimed, but it must hit where you look. Rather than adjusting sights, you need proper fit.

Pace off a distance compatible with your shotgun's choke—40 yards for full choke, 30 for modified and about 22 yards for improved cylinder. Then put up a large sheet of paper with a dark mark in the middle. Mount your shotgun as you normally would afield and fire at the mark. The resulting pattern should spread evenly around it in a rough circle. Several shots and sheets of paper should give you an average.

If your patterns are too high, your stock may be too straight for you or too long. If the patterns are too low, your stock may have too much drop (the measurement from the middle of the top of your stock to a flat surface against which the top of the barrel and receiver are held). Generally, standard field stock dimensions will fit most shooters with sleeve lengths between 31 and 33 inches.

A gunsmith can shorten your stock if necessary, or lengthen it by adding a recoil pad and butt spacers. He can also alter the amount of drop if this is a problem. When a shotgun shoots consistently to the left or right, it may mean the shooter is not mounting it so that he is looking straight down the barrel. Occasionally, this can also result from a barrel that has been bent or damaged. A gunsmith can check this out for you.

A properly fitted shotgun is the same as a correctly zeroed-in rifle or handgun. Always take time to make sure the gun you use is zeroed-in.

DESIGNED TO CATCH both plastic practice rounds and lead bullets and pellets, this easily constructed target box uses a hinged inner deflector.

INNER-HINGED and steel-shielded door lifts to snap into cabinet latch. Then it acts to deflect bullets into sand layer in the bottom.

LOWERED DOOR acts as floor of box when reusable plastic bullets are used. The bullets strike a towel backstop, then fall undamaged to the bottom of box.

Target box serves double duty

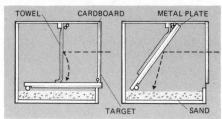

BACK, 1/2 x 11 x 16-3/4"
CLEAT
TOP, 1/4 x 12 x 18"
SWINGING DOOR, 1/2 x 11-3/8 x 16-1/2"
2-1/2"
3-1/2"
BOTTOM, 1/2 x 11 x 17"
SIDE, 1/2 x 16-3/4 x 18" (2 REQD.)
1/2 x 3-1/2 x 11"

TOWEL   CARDBOARD   METAL PLATE
TARGET   SAND

■ A SWINGING DOOR is the unique feature of this simple target box. With metal boiler plate or sheet-metal door in 45° up position, pellets and lead bullets are deflected down into a sand cushion in the bottom of the box. With the door tilted down to floor the box, a folded bath towel hangs midway back to stop plastic pellet practice rounds so that they are undamaged and can be collected and reused after the indoor or outdoor shooting.

The simple ½-inch-plywood box can be built in any size. As shown, it easily mounts standard pistol targets on a piece of corrugated cardboard stapled over the front of the box. The swinging door hinges on a dowel and is held up by a cabinet latch. Mount a carrying handle on the top of the target box.

FOR BENCH-REST competition, massive concrete benches of special design provide support for weighty rifles.

Ultimate test for your rifle

■ MANY A SHOOTER takes his trusty rifle, fires a few shots at a gallon can or similar target and figures he knows just how his gun is zeroed in. If he hits the can a couple of times in four or five shots at 50 yards, he figures he's ready for the range or the deer season. He does his shooting while standing, or leaning against a tree, or resting across the hood of his car or from some other haphazard position.

But shooting that way does not give a true picture of the accuracy of either gun or shooter, and doesn't really indicate whether the gun is sighted-in properly. More important, it can give a false picture of the potential accuracy of the gun, and might jeopardize an important and expensive hunt as well. There is a better way.

The absolute tops in rifle accuracy is produced by a rather small group of enthusiasts belonging to the National Bench Rest Shooters Assn. (NBRSA). Even the most casual shooter can benefit from the methods they use to shoot five and 10-shot groups that are often indistinguishable from a single bullet hole.

These bench-resters measure their groups (from center to center of the most widely separated holes) with sophisticated optical instruments. Groups shot at 100 yards have been recorded with measurements that are less than $\frac{1}{10}$ inch between centers of the widest shots. That beats legendary tack-driving by a considerable margin.

This degree of accuracy is obtained with specially built guns, very precisely hand-loaded ammunition, unusual shooting techniques, and a rigid shooting table, called a bench rest, with sandbag or mechanical supports on it.

Accuracy for the rest of us

The special guns aren't suitable for the hunter, but bench-resters do shoot a category of "sporter" rifles that are quite suitable for hunting. The specially loaded ammunition is usually out, too, because the average hunter normally shoots only factory cartridges. He can, however, borrow bench-rest techniques to better prepare himself and his rifle for that important big-game hunt.

First comes the shooting bench, or *bench rest*. Many ranges have benches of one sort or another, but they usually aren't the massive, reinforced-concrete or timber structures of the pure bench-rest range. As long as they are solid, they'll do, and if there aren't any available you can make up a simple portable bench as shown in the drawing. It won't cost much and will last a lifetime, improving your shooting every time it's used. The splayed legs give it a firm foundation, and it is further stabilized by the weight of your torso, the rifle and sandbags. This combined weight will give your rifle a firm, solid surface.

Those bags

With any bench, you'll need sandbags. They can be bought in cheap or expensive models, of course, but it's also simple to make your own. Any close-woven strong cloth will serve.

Two or three rectangular bags 12 to 16 inches long and about six inches wide will serve up front. A couple of smaller bags will do back at the butt; often one is sufficient. Bags should be loosely filled so they can easily be squeezed to shape. Filled tightly, they won't work as well. Clean sand is the common filler, but lead shot is preferred by some shooters, in spite of its cost.

The large bags are stacked up near the front edge of the bench to support the fore-end of the rifle. The fore-end is bedded down into the top bag for the lateral as well as vertical support. Place the smaller bag(s) under the toe of the rifle butt, bedding the stock into it.

With malleable sandbags under the gun at both ends, the rifle's vertical angle can be changed easily to align the sights on target. Major changes are made in the front bags; minor ones by squeezing the rear bag with the left hand to raise or lower the butt slightly. In this manner, the sights are brought to bear on the target and all vertical support comes from the sandbags, eliminating the trembling and weaving present when the support comes only from your body. Lateral changes are made by moving the front bags or the rifle on them; minor shifts again by squeezing or moving the rear bag.

Hunting rifles generally recoil more forcefully than heavy bench-rest guns so the hunter must support the butt solidly with his shoulder. Alternately, a 25-pound bag of lead shot can be placed between gun butt and shoulder. This reduces recoil movement of the gun, eases the blow on your shoulder, and damps out shoulder movement.

HEAVY WEIGHT and small caliber of bench-rest rifle dampen recoil and make unnecessary shooter's shoulder support.

COMBINING SANDBAGS and a mechanical support to benchrest a hunting rifle, hunter test-fires the gun to check its sights and accuracy.

HEAVY STEEL channel serves as stock for this unlimited-class specialty rifle. Shooter, like many bench-resters, brings along reloading equipment.

MASSIVE BENCH-REST model can be held by sandbags, mechanical supports as shown, or elaborate return-to-battery mounts that return to aim-point.

With this understood, here's how the shooting goes. First, as always, make certain the rifle is *unloaded.* Seat yourself at the bench, adjusting seat height so that your left forearm and right elbow (if you shoot right-handed) can rest comfortably on the bench top. Then adjust the sandbags so the rifle points at the target when solidly bedded and you can see clearly through the sights without muscular strain. Grasp the rear sandbag with the left hand and make minor adjustments by squeezing and shifting it to bring the sights dead-on. Don't try to shift the gun by nudging it around with your shoulder. The left hand shouldn't touch the gun, just the sandbag.

With sight alignment correct, support the butt solidly with your shoulder, but don't disrupt the rifle's seat in the sandbags. Grasp the trigger grip of the stock firmly but gently with your right

PORTABLE BENCH can be easily made to help you test your gun and improve your shooting. It has splayed legs to give it a firm foundation that is further stabilized by your weight and sandbags. It can be quickly taken apart and then reassembled in the field for an accuracy check.

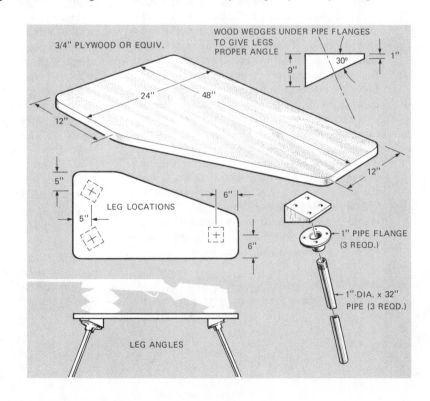

hand. Squeeze the trigger carefully to fire, without disturbing that solid sandbag support. At first, do this dry-fire without loading the gun. The hammer or striker should fall without any disturbance of sight/target alignment. Practice this a bit before stepping up to live shooting.

So long as you've bedded the rifle well on the sandbags and don't disturb it with your shoulder or when pulling the trigger, the human error present in other forms of shooting is very nearly eliminated. Thus you'll be able to shoot accurately, and what shows up on your target represents the mechanical accuracy of only your rifle and ammunition.

Of course you must still control your breathing and keep your body as still as possible. By being firmly seated and resting your arms and torso solidly on the bench, such control becomes easy. *Any* movement of your arms, hands or upper body will be transmitted to the gun. If you note a very slight but regular twitch of the gun as you concentrate on the sights and target, it is most likely the effect of your pulse. This can come from the carotid artery in your neck and can be eliminated by carefully shifting your head and neck.

Fire!

When sights and target stay in rock-steady alignment while the trigger is squeezed, you're ready for live ammunition. Load with one cartridge, get everything in position, align the sights and squeeze off a shot. Jack out the empty, relax, and then repeat the process for at least three to five shots at one to two-minute intervals. This keeps the barrel from heating rapidly, which can cause it to bend slightly, affecting the bullet's strike zone. Since the first shot is the most important to the hunter, the barrel should be kept relatively cool, simulating first-shot field conditions. Take care to position both rifle and yourself back *exactly* the same for each shot. Recoil will move the gun to the rear, and it must be repositioned on the sandbags before firing again. "Exactly" means just that. Deviations in position, bedding in the bags, grip on the stock or snugness of your shoulder to the butt will reduce accuracy.

Study the grouping

Once you have fired a group of three to five shots from the bench you'll see clearly how well your gun is targeted, as well as just how accurately it can shoot. You may be surprised to find the sights weren't zeroed as closely as you thought. If the group isn't on point of aim, now is the time to shift the sights and then shoot another group to check them. In fact, you may need to shoot several groups to get the sights set exactly, and in doing so you'll learn more about just how much accuracy your gun can deliver.

Half a dozen groups will show what normally can be expected from your gun and ammunition alone. Average group size will indicate the smallest target that can be hit consistently without usual human error. Make allowance for your error and instability under hunting conditions and you'll realize that an offhand shot at a deer 300 yards away is a waste of time unless you and the gun are both exceptionally good.

Bonus benefits

The use of a bench rest and related shooting methods are equally helpful regardless of the type or calibre rifle (or even handgun) that you shoot and the type of sights it carries. The light, open-sighted .22 rimfire squirrel or rabbit rifle is, in fact, less likely to be properly zeroed than a big-game rifle. Further, the usual targets of such a rifle are smaller so that one needs first-class hunt preparation.

Bench-rest enthusiasts shoot with high-magnification scope sights and use very small square black aiming points. They either quarter the square with the scope cross hairs or set the square in an angle formed by the intersecting cross hairs. Hunting scopes are usually of only 2½X to 6X power so a larger aiming point like a two-inch or four-inch square is much easier to use. With iron sights, open or peep, you may require an even larger aiming point, and a circular shape is better than a square.

Vary the range

While the bench experts shoot only at fixed ranges of 100, 200 and 300 yards, your bench-rest work may be done at any range that suits the space available or approximates the range you normally shoot. And bench-resting before the hunting season or any other time is bound to increase your accuracy and enjoyment of the sport.

INDEX · VOLUME 15

SHOP GUIDE

CUSTOMARY TO METRIC (CONVERSION) Conversion factors can be carried so far they become impractical. In cases below where an entry is exact it is followed by an asterisk (*). Where considerable rounding off has taken place, the entry is followed by a + or a − sign.

Linear Measure

inches	millimeters
1/16	1.5875*
1/8	3.2
3/16	4.8
1/4	6.35*
5/16	7.9
3/8	9.5
7/16	11.1
1/2	12.7*
9/16	14.3
5/8	15.9
11/16	17.5
3/4	19.05*
13/16	20.6
7/8	22.2
15/16	23.8
1	25.4*

inches	centimeters
1	2.54*
2	5.1
3	7.6
4	10.2
5	12.7*
6	15.2
7	17.8
8	20.3
9	22.9
10	25.4*
11	27.9
12	30.5

feet	centimeters	meters
1	30.48*	.3048*
2	61	.61
3	91	.91
4	122	1.22
5	152	1.52
6	183	1.83
7	213	2.13
8	244	2.44
9	274	2.74
10	305	3.05
50	1524*	15.24*
100	3048*	30.48*

1 yard = .9144* meters
1 rod = 5.0292* meters
1 mile = 1.6 kilometers
1 nautical mile = 1.852* kilometers

Weights

ounces	grams
1	28.3
2	56.7
3	85
4	113
5	142
6	170
7	198
8	227
9	255
10	283
11	312
12	340
13	369
14	397
15	425
16	454

Formula (exact):
ounces × 28.349 523 125* = grams

pounds	kilograms
1	.45
2	.9
3	1.4
4	1.8
5	2.3
6	2.7
7	3.2
8	3.6
9	4.1
10	4.5

1 short ton (2000 lbs) = 907 kilograms (kg)
Formula (exact):
pounds × .453 592 37* = kilograms

Fluid Measure

(Milliliters [ml] and cubic centimeters [cc] are equivalent, but it is customary to use milliliters for liquids.)

1 cu in	=	16.39 ml
1 fl oz	=	29.6 ml
1 cup	=	237 ml
1 pint	=	473 ml
1 quart	=	946 ml
	=	.946 liters
1 gallon	=	3785 ml
	=	3.785 liters

Formula (exact):
fluid ounces × 29.573 529 562 5*
= milliliters

Volume

1 cu in	=	16.39 cubic centimeters (cc)
1 cu ft	=	28 316.7 cc
1 bushel	=	35 239.1 cc
1 peck	=	8 809.8 cc

Area

1 sq in	=	6.45 sq cm
1 sq ft	=	929 sq cm
	=	.093 sq meters
1 sq yd	=	.84 sq meters
1 acre	=	4 046.9 sq meters
	=	.404 7 hectares
1 sq mile	=	2 589 988 sq meters
	=	259 hectares
	=	2.589 9 sq kilometers

Miscellaneous

1 British thermal unit (Btu) (mean)
= 1 055.9 joules
1 horsepower = 745.7 watts
= .75 kilowatts
caliber (diameter of a firearm's bore in hundredths of an inch)
= .254 millimeters (mm)

1 atmosphere pressure = 101 325* pascals (newtons per sq meter)
1 pound per square inch (psi) = 6 895 pascals
1 pound per square foot = 47.9 pascals
1 knot = 1.85 kilometers per hour
1 mile per hour = 1.6093 kilometers per hour